WILLIAM FAULKNER

THE WILLIAM B. WISDOM COLLECTION

IN THE

HOWARD-TILTON MEMORIAL LIBRARY

TULANE UNIVERSITY

William Faulkner by Lamarr Stephens, 1948.

WILLIAM FAULKNER

THE WILLIAM B. WISDOM COLLECTION:
A DESCRIPTIVE CATALOGUE

Compiled with an introduction by
THOMAS BONNER, JR.

Edited by
GUILLERMO NÁÑEZ FALCÓN

Essays by
CLEANTH BROOKS and CARVEL COLLINS

THE TULANE UNIVERSITY LIBRARIES
New Orleans, 1980

Library of Congress Cataloging in Publication Data

Tulane University of Louisiana. Howard-Tilton Memorial Library.
William Faulkner, the William B. Wisdom Collection.

   Chiefly a catalog of the Wisdom Collection in the Tulane University Library.

   1. Faulkner, William, 1897-1962—Manuscripts—Catalogs. 2.
Faulkner, William, 1897-1962—Bibliography—Catalogs. 3. Wis-
dom, William B., 1900-1977—Library. I. Wisdom, William B.,
1900-1977. II. Bonner, Thomas, Jr., 1942-   III. Náñez Falcón,
Guillermo. IV. Brooks, Cleanth, 1906-   V. Collins, Carvel
Emerson, 1912-   VI. Title.
PS3511.A86Z9775   1980   016.813'5'2   79-26556

ISBN 0-9603212-2-5

In Memory

of

WILLIAM B. WISDOM

1900-1977

Funds for this publication were provided
through the courtesy of
The Friends of the Tulane University Library

CONTENTS

WILLIAM B. WISDOM: THE MAN AND HIS COLLECTION

THE WILLIAM B. WISDOM COLLECTION OF WILLIAM FAULKNER

Part One: Works by Faulkner

TABLE OF CONTENTS (Continued)

Page

CHECKLIST OF OTHER FAULKNER MATERIALS IN THE TULANE UNIVERSITY LIBRARY

Works by Faulkner

Works About Faulkner

WILLIAM B. WISDOM: THE MAN AND HIS COLLECTION

INTRODUCTION

by Thomas Bonner, Jr.

In 1970 William B. Wisdom presented Tulane University with a collection of works by and about William Faulkner. Mr. Wisdom, who had previously donated his Thomas Wolfe collection to Harvard University, retained some authority over accessibility. By 1977, Cleanth Brooks and Carvel Collins had used the Tulane collection. Although Joseph Blotner acknowledges the aid of Mr. Wisdom in his biography of Faulkner, there is no indication that he had been given access to the materials. The first public exhibition of selected items occurred in December, 1976, when the Friends of the Library of Tulane University celebrated the organization's establishment. After the death of Mr. Wisdom, Mrs. Ann S. Gwyn, Head of Special Collections at the Tulane University Library, approved the cataloguing of the collection and arranged to have it published as a suitable memorial to such a munificent benefactor. Subsequently, Tulane's Friends of the Library announced their sponsorship of a memorial publication.

The Wisdom Collection consists of over 370 individually catalogued items by and about Faulkner; it includes manuscripts, manuscript books, typescripts, unpublished letters and photographs, recordings, editions, criticism, and biographical materials. Counting duplicates, the total has now risen to over 550, and because of the generosity of the friends of Mr. Wisdom and the Friends of the Library, the collection continues to grow.

Among the manuscripts, the two manuscript books *Mayday* and *Helen: A Courtship* are especially important. *Mayday* is an Arthurian prose narrative, which includes such common elements as visions, a quest, love, and allegory. Both the subject and the language are "romantic" as the following passages indicate: Sir Galwyn observes in the waters "one all young and white, and with long shining hair"; he thinks of "young hyacinths in spring, and honey and sunlight"; and he becomes "as one sinking from a

[1]

fever into a soft and bottomless sleep." Galwyn then enters the waters. The dialogue, however, is not all romantic; here Princess Aelia responds to a compliment: "Why do you really think I am beautiful? . . . . I am sorry you saw me in this rag. I hate yellow; it makes me look—oh—fat, and I am not fat." The forty-three page book was handbound, written, and illustrated by Faulkner, who dedicated it to Helen Baird—"To thee/ O wise and lovely." The place and date of composition are "OXFORD, MISSISSIPPI, 27 JANUARY, 1926." The illustrations include two black-and-white drawings as endpapers, three full-page watercolors, five emblazoned letters, and a heraldic device at the conclusion. The cloth-backed papers-over-boards cover has a marble-like pattern of blue, green, and yellow colors with a paper label for the title. The hand-printing on textured paper is distinguished by the archaic "v" for "u" and the "s" reversed in direction.

A facsimile edition of *Mayday* was printed and handbound by the University of Notre Dame Press in 1977 in a limited number and published in a trade edition since. Criticism on *Mayday* can be found in Carvel Collins' separately bound essay accompanying the facsimile and in the introduction to the trade edition. Cleanth Brooks' essay "The Image of Helen Baird in Faulkner's Early Prose, Poetry, and Fiction" (*Sewanee Review*/Spring 1977) and his book *William Faulkner: Toward Yoknapatawpha and Beyond* include discussions of *Mayday*.

After *Mayday*, Faulkner wrote a second book dedicated to Helen Baird, whom he courted in New Orleans and Pascagoula, but without success. *Helen: A Courtship* was handbound and handprinted, the date and place of composition described as "Oxford Mississippi, June 1926." This eighteen-leaf book begins with a dedicatory poem, "To Helen, Swimming," followed by fifteen sonnets. Each poem has a date and a place of composition. Dates range from June to September of 1925. The places include Pascagoula, Majorca, Genoa, Pavia, Lago Maggiore, and Paris. The poems are distinctly romantic and youthful in tone and choice of subject as the following first lines indicate: "Beneath the apple tree Eve's tortured shape"; "With laggard March, a faun whose ring"; and "Knew I love once? Was it love or grief." The cloth-backed papers-over-boards cover has a marble-like pattern of blue, red, purple, gold, and orange with a paper label for the title. Each poem is on the recto of a page. The handprinting corresponds with that of *Mayday* with the eccentric use of "v" for "u" and the "s" reversed in direction on textured paper. Brooks observes that only five of these poems have been reprinted—II, III, IV, V, VI (numbers from the text).

Other manuscripts in the Wisdom Collection include two untitled poems similar to those inspired by Helen Baird. One holograph of ten lines on lined paper reads as follows:

> Behind the masque—a maiden's face
>> In the eyes a girl appears
> Through the eyes the soul looks out
>> A miracle, a thing of grace
> Yet as I stared, the girl was gone
> And there was left—the withered crone
> The miracle I saw was done
> Mask and soul now were one
> Behind the mask—a maiden's face
>> In the eyes a girl appears.

The page contains neither date nor signature, but the handwriting, style, and choice of subject are unmistakably those of Faulkner.

A second poem in holograph contains nine lines written on lined paper. It is accompanied by an artist's sketch, possibly a caricature of himself. The poem is a romantic compliment to a young lady, described as a Frost-like "birch tree in a dusky wood":

> She is like a tower of warm ivory
> With the pale ashes of a dead fire
> For hair
> Her eyes are like a misty forest at dawn
> She is like a birch tree in a dusky wood
> A poplar bending slenderly
> To receive upon her face the moon's kiss.
>
> She is also
> The mistress of my friend.

This poem with the riddle-like conclusion is undated, but it does bear the signature "William Falkner."

[3]

Among the letters in manuscript are several to **Helen Baird**. One, written on stationery from the Beverly **Hills Hotel**, has Faulkner's signature but no date; in it the writer laments that he missed seeing Helen in New Orleans but that he plans to see her later. After commenting on the beautiful weather, he writes, "Wish I had my horse. I wouldn't mind these jobs if I had a horse." Another letter, this one undated and unsigned, predicts a fruitful writing period ahead, one similar to a past time in Pascagoula. A third letter reveals "odds and ends of stories and notes in a wooden box in the smokehouse under a lot of trash and such, which I still intend to exhume and look through." A typed letter to Miss Baird includes a memorable description of her: "I remember a sullen-jawed yellow-eyed belligerent humorless gal in a linen dress and sunburned bare legs sitting on Spratling's balcony and not thinking even a hell of a little bit of me that afternoon, maybe already decided not to. But damn letters anyway."

Unfortunately, there is no complete typescript of a Faulkner novel in the collection. However, the original and revised typescripts of Chapter One of *Absalom, Absalom!*, both of which were sent to *American Mercury* for its works-in-progress series, are included. The chapter as published in the novel is considerably different from that which appeared in the magazine. The original typescript has significant corrections and deletions, but the revised version bears only a proofreader's marks. A significant example of a deleted section is the conversation between "the two separate Quentins now talking to one another in the long silence of not people, in not language . . . ." And this is one of the smaller deletions.

Of the seven typescripts of published stories, all have been reprinted. "The Mirror of Chartres Street/No. 7" is an original typescript with corrections and changes. Having appeared originally in *The Double Dealer* and reprinted in *New Orleans Sketches*, it is more of a descriptive and imaginative series of sketches than a story, and includes such diverse figures as a wealthy Jew, a priest, and a longshoreman among others. The remaining stories all made their first appearances in *American Mercury* and show varying degrees of corrections and deletions: "Centaur in Brass," which is part of the Snopes material incorporated into *The Town;* "Golden

Land," which experiments with typography; "Hair," the central character of which, Maxey the barber, appears in *Light in August;* "Pennsylvania Station," which is set in New York and involves the building of a coffin; "That Will Be Fine," which is set at Christmas in Mottstown, "up from Jefferson"; and "Uncle Willy," which centers on a morphine addict who finally manages to fly— in his own plane.

Other material by Faulkner includes recordings, drawings, a screenplay, and notes. The two recordings of Faulkner reading from *Light in August* and *The Bear* were made at the National Broadcasting Company, New York City, on April 27, 1956. The drawings are from *Ole Miss* and *The Scream,* which listed Faulkner on the art staff. Both are publications of the University of Mississippi. A mimeograph copy of the final screenplay, "The Left Hand of God," is dated July 18, 1952. A minor but not insignificant item is a Xerox copy of Faulkner's recipe for curing meat.

Of the printed works by Faulkner, it is important to note the uncorrected proof of *A Fable,* first edition, first printings of *Soldiers' Pay, Mosquitoes,* and *The Sound and the Fury.* First editions, first printings of poetry are *A Green Bough, The Marble Faun,* and *This Earth.* Also of interest are *Sherwood Anderson & Other Famous Creoles: A Gallery of Contemporary New Orleans* and the Spiral Press edition *William Faulkner's Speech of Acceptance upon the Award of the Nobel Prize for Literature.* All of Faulkner's major editions, many signed by the author, are in the collection, along with a considerable number of translations in French, German, Yugoslavian, and Japanese to cite a few.

Fortunately, the literary criticism in the Wisdom Collection and in the other collections of the Tulane Library is comprehensive with only a few items of special interest cited here. A typescript of Cleanth Brooks' essay "Faulkner as Poet," dated April 29, 1969, indicates Faulkner's poetic debt to Swinburne, Verlaine, and Housman among others. A mimeograph copy of Robert Penn Warren's "William Faulkner and His South," delivered at the University of Virginia on March 13, 1951, is an early essay on Faulkner's concern with good and evil. Carvel Collins' introduction to *Mayday* is indispensable to those readers interested in circumstances of its writing and its relationship to Faulkner's other works. Evelyn Scott's *On William Faulkner's The Sound and the Fury,* which was published in 1929 as a ten-page pamphlet, approaches the novel as a tragedy. It is perhaps the first critical essay other than a review of this novel.

Biographical materials in the Wisdom Collection and in the other divisions of the Library include a substantial collection of books and journals along with a large number of special newspaper issues on Faulkner. The collection also includes the uncorrected proofs of Meta Carpenter Wilde's *A Loving Gentleman: The Love Story of William Faulkner and Meta Carpenter* and a group of formal and informal photographs of Faulkner by Professor Lamarr Stephens of Tulane University. Several show the novelist at the helm of his sailboat on Lake Sardis. Helen Baird Lyman's 20x16 inch oil portrait of Faulkner is an item of unusual interest; one should note Carvel Collins' comments on this work in his essay in this volume. Professor Bell I. Wiley's note offers an eyewitness account of Faulkner's address on segregation at the meeting of the Southern Historical Association in Memphis, Tennessee, on November 10, 1955.

Although it is difficult to assess the full value of this collection, several eminent scholars have already attested to its quality. James Meriwether has described it as a "very major collection . . . . the best William Faulkner collection in private hands." Cleanth Brooks, in the preface to *Toward Yoknapatawpha and Beyond,* cites "the unique Faulkner items" in the collection; in his commentary for this volume he writes: "this collection constitutes a real treasure trove . . . . much more than a first-rate working library." Carvel Collins in his essay in this volume observes: "The unique New Orleans materials which Mr. Wisdom gathered are a magnificent capstone to his fine collection."

As every serious student of literature knows, William Faulkner explored time in its manifold perspectives. And many readers have spent considerable time, themselves, reading poems, essays, and books by and about Faulkner, responding as fully as possible to his unique art. This collection will prolong that response and make even more ironic the printed announcement now in the collection, but which had been posted in Oxford, Mississippi, on the day of

[6]

his funeral: "In Memory of William Faulkner This Business Will Be Closed From 2:00 to 2:15 P.M. Today, July 7, 1962."

Acknowledgements: My gratitude goes to Mrs. Jill Faulkner Summers for permission to quote from her father's unpublished works; and to Professor Lamarr Stephens for the photographs reproduced in this volume; and to Cleanth Brooks and Carvel Collins for their essays and assistance. I thank the Friends of the Tulane University Library for the support needed to make this work a reality. Special thanks go to Mrs. Ann S. Gwyn, Head of the Special Collections Division of the Tulane University Library and project director of this publication, for her encouragement and considerable co-operation; to Dr. Guillermo Náñez Falcón, also of the Special Collections Division, for his indispensable editorial assistance; and to the other staff members of this Division for their many kindnesses. Professor Earl N. Harbert of Tulane University deserves mention for his sound counsel. Emeritus Professor Joseph Patrick Roppolo of Tulane University has continued to advise me. The late Professor Richard P. Adams of Tulane University is remembered here for his inspiration of Faulkner studies. And I thank my wife Judith for her assistance.

Xavier University
New Orleans, Louisiana

WILLIAM B. WISDOM

A MEMOIR — WILLIAM B. WISDOM, COLLECTOR

by Carvel Collins

It is pleasant to be invited to supply a personal memoir of William B. Wisdom as a collector of Faulkner, for a top-notch collector he certainly was. In the 1940's I began to hear his name while using now and then the astonishingly thorough collection of Thomas Wolfe materials which he had given to Harvard's Houghton Library. The Director of that Library, William Jackson, often spoke admiringly of Mr. Wisdom in our various professional and social meetings, and after dinner one evening near the end of October, 1948, reported that he had just returned from New Orleans where Mr. Wisdom had shown him several William Faulkner items, including two booklets hand-lettered by the author. He said he had told Mr. Wisdom that one of the courses I was teaching that autumn was given over exclusively to Faulkner's works and had asked whether he would show his Faulkner collection to me. With such support I wrote to Mr. Wisdom on November 2, 1948, and received a prompt and generous reply dated November 5. That exchange initiated an association which lasted twenty-eight years and, according to the records I have, included more than a hundred and fifty letters between us, a few telegrams, several meetings at New Orleans, and valuable help of every kind by Mr. Wisdom.

He was a collector with perception, dedication, high standards, and generosity. Perceptively he had begun to gather materials on Faulkner before Faulkner—receiving the Nobel Prize in 1950— became overnight the subject of that flood of critical and bio- graphical studies which inundated academia. Mr. Wisdom kept up other collecting interests as well, adding to the superb Tom Wolfe materials and to his rich materials at opposite ends of the Louisiana spectrum: the history of Carnival in New Orleans and the career of Huey Long. In 1964 he wrote, ". . . I have turned my attention in the last two years to collecting original sources, first editions in

French mostly, on the settlement of Louisiana." With gifts from among those and other rare materials as well as his Faulkner collection he has been a major benefactor of the Special Collections Division in the Howard-Tilton Library at Tulane University, as Mrs. Ann S. Gwyn, the excellent Head of that division, always has been pleased to point out.

Collecting—the chase—was a joy to him. In one of his letters describing some important materials which he was glad to have just come upon after having temporarily mislaid them, he too modestly added, "So-o-o-o, I may not be the most methodical and bibliographical and scientific collector in the world, but I'll bet I have more fun." For a time he wondered how I could bring myself to spend years gathering just information rather than first editions, but an unbelievably lucky afternoon we had together— an afternoon we later often mentioned to each other with amazement—changed that. At lunch he hesitantly had offered to help me with interviews that day if I felt he could be useful. I was delighted, and we began phoning possible New Orleans friends and acquaintances of Faulkner whose names I had on a list. To our mutual astonishment every one of them was at home, willing to give an interview, full of firm recollections, articulate, open-handed with documents, and eager to name more people we should see that day. And the timing was so uncharacteristically smooth that we efficiently raced through the Quarter directly from one interview to another all afternoon, only pausing to interrogate additional Faulkner acquaintances whom, with the same magical good fortune, we bumped into on the streets. That evening he said he now knew that the chase is the chase whether or not the quarry is three-dimensional.

He was a collector with high standards both for the physical condition of rare items and for the quality of critical and scholarly writings. One extreme demonstration of his concern for good condition comes to mind immediately: A family, who had become friends as I talked with them over the years about Faulkner, asked advice concerning selling a group of partially burned Faulkner documents which remained after the sale of a much larger group which had been less hurt by the fire. Because Mr. Wisdom always said he would like to know whenever anyone had Faulkner materials for sale, I wrote him about the papers and the damage to them. He replied, "This is not a letter. This is in haste . . . Please mail me the charred poems so I can examine them." After he opened the package he wrote at once, "I feel like I am sitting on top of an atomic bomb . . . was aghast at the fragility of the sheets. To be absolutely truthful, I looked at the top sheet . . . and I was so terrified by its friability that I hastily replaced it on top of the pile with tremulous hands . . . I would not touch such an easily damaged irreplaceable relic with a ten foot pole . . . My immediate problem is how to get it back to you . . . I hesitate to entrust it to the mails . . . Now that my immediate reactions have been made clear, I must tell you how deeply I appreciate . . . the opportunity to look at these priceless pages."

He sometimes said he felt that too much of what was being published about Faulkner was not up to the standard of criticism and scholarship he always hoped for. In one of his letters he wrote that he hated to see "inadequate critics dilute the Faulkner atmosphere with their incompetent and abtuse criticism." And in another, that there were too many "writers cluttering the Faulkner shelves with puny efforts. Even a respected critic . . . launched his boat from the wrong premises. All this tatterdemalia is going to make the public tired of Faulkner's name . . . ." Nevertheless he wholeheartedly favored criticism and scholarship and wished them well. One of his hopes was that someone would bring out a full-scale Faulkner bibliography; so he spoke with genuine disappointment in one of our last conversations when he said he had concluded that no such work would appear in the foreseeable future.

He was, as I said, generous. He gave not only financial support but his time and effective attention to work of all kinds, ranging from helping restore the Cabildo to helping improve the functioning of the New Orleans public library system. In connection with his concern for the library he sent in July, 1963, this telegram:

AS A MEMBER OF THE PUBLIC LIBRARY BOARD I AM UP TO MY NECK IN DEFENDING JAMES BALDWINS ANOTHER COUNTRY FROM BEING BANNED BY THE CITY ATTORNEYS OFFICE AND THE POLICE DEPARTMENT. COULD YOU POS-

[11]

SIBLY SEND ME A CHECK LIST OF UNIVERSITIES
AND COLLEGES WHICH IN THEIR COURSES IN
AMERICAN LITERATURE STUDY JAMES BALDWIN
AND REQUIRE . . . ANOTHER COUNTRY AS COL-
LATERAL READING OR AS AN INTEGRAL PART
OF THE COURSE. THIS IS A LARGE ORDER BUT
IF YOU COULD DROP IT TO ME AIR MAIL IT
WILL BE A BIG HELP BEST REGARDS

He generously made his Faulkner collection available to me
at any time and for any use I wanted to put it to. And he went
beyond that in many ways. He bid at auction for materials he
thought would be helpful to me. For years he voluntarily reserved
major items for my exclusive use. When I wrote him that a scholar
wanted access to the complete typescript of a Faulkner piece which
had been cut by an editor and that he might want to grant it, he
replied, on May 21, 1964, ". . . I have no idea of letting him or
anyone else have access . . . I do not propose to dilute to the
tiniest degree your efforts in that field, by assisting other critics or
biographers." He gave energy, time, attention, and judgment whenever publishing presented problems about the texts of some of
Faulkner's early works. He would compare various originals available not only in his collection but in other New Orleans files,
always with a strong desire to help make possible more nearly
accurate texts, though he somewhat shared Edmund Wilson's views
after large federal subsidies caused several university literature de-
partments, as one wag said, to replace the New Criticism by the
New Proofreading, with an accurate text sometimes becoming the
final goal of literary labor rather than the basis for beginning.
He would query New Orleans friends about biographical details
he knew I was puzzling over. And at one point, after several times
having asked me courteously in a non-intrusive way how I was
financing a prolonged expensive investigation, sent with no warn-
ing an envelope out of which dropped a most useful check for
research expenses from a foundation he had established.

Typical of his generosities was helping to arrange my first
interview with Mrs. Helen Baird Lyman, in 1954, and saying early
that when the timing was right I should edit facsimiles of what he

sometimes called his two "uniquities," *Mayday* and *Helen: A Courtship,* the gift booklets for Helen Baird which Faulkner hand-lettered and bound in 1926. Later when I brought the matter up again, in 1963, he replied that I should direct "tentative overtures, trial balloons and timid suggestions" to the Faulkner Estate. He went on to say facsimile publication might change the value of an original one way or the other but that was "beside the point since our primary consideration is the enhancement and the illumination of Faulkner's genius." Years later, in our next-to-last meeting, we finally concluded an agreement to publish the facsimile of *Mayday* and a later trade edition, though the timing turned out to be wrong after all, because the facsimile unfortunately did not appear until shortly after his death.

Such a relationship cannot be allowed to be *totally* a one-way street; so I was pleased through the years to be able now and then to send him a modest but elusive Faulkner document or tape recording or the whereabouts of an unknown publication by Faulkner which he might want to buy or any lead I heard of to Faulkner documents held by people living in New Orleans. It was pleasant to be able to send for his collection a portrait of Faulkner done in oils by Mrs. Helen Baird Lyman. The portrait—in which Faulkner, interestingly enough, appears much older than he actually looked at that time—was painted by Mrs. Lyman in 1955, exactly thirty years after Faulkner had asked her to marry him and immediately after a brief and surely dramatic chance meeting with Faulkner and a young woman on the nearly empty winter beach at Pascagoula. I had enjoyed having it on the wall after a good friend of Mrs. Lyman's kindly gave it to me, but because the Wisdom collection contained among its New Orleans items the gift booklets and letters which Faulkner had sent to Helen Baird, it seemed the logical permanent place for the portrait, and much safer.

The unique New Orleans materials which Mr. Wisdom gathered are a magnificent capstone to his fine collection, for it was at New Orleans in the middle of the nineteen twenties that Faulkner shifted his concentration from poetry to the fiction for which many critics, worldwide, have come to consider him the best novelist the United States has produced so far in this century. Mr. Wisdom got those materials together with admirably imaginative dedication, and it was a privilege to be allowed to watch him gather some of them and to profit professionally from his generosity with them all. In ending this personal recollection it also must be said that one of the greatest among the generous gifts which William B. Wisdom gave was pleasure—in his quick intelligence, his wit, and his being always the best of company.

THE FAULKNER MANUSCRIPTS AND TYPESCRIPTS IN THE WISDOM COLLECTION

by Cleanth Brooks

The size and quality of the William B. Wisdom Collection of Faulkner manuscripts, typescripts, and printed volumes speaks for itself. One does not have to be an experienced bibliographer or even widely read in Faulkner in order to perceive that this collection constitutes a real treasure trove.

Accordingly, in a brief note such as this, I shall not undertake to comment on every item catalogued. The reader can see for himself how rich and varied the collection is. But it may not be amiss to point out that even items such as the original typescripts of published works possess more than a sentimental interest. Even when they contain only "light corrections" and deletions, they possess an interest for scholars.

Ours is an age much concerned to achieve accurate and authentic texts of our noteworthy literary works. The ideal is to distinguish, when possible, the various stages of the development of a text from the first draft to the author's final corrections. Thus, even manuscripts and typescripts that offer only the minimum information of this sort are, nevertheless, worth the attention of the textual scholar.

The fact that the Wisdom Collection contains material of this sort, together with the presence of Faulkner first editions and copies of the principal commentaries on Faulkner would render this collection an excellent working library for any student of Faulkner. But the Wisdom Collection is much more than a first-rate working library.

What gives it special importance are the several unique documents that it contains—items that are simply to be found nowhere else and that constitute a magnet calculated to attract Faulkner scholars from all over the world. The most notable of them—the two little hand-lettered booklets written for Helen Baird, *Mayday*

[15]

and *Helen: A Courtship,* and five letters to her—throw a special light on an important period in Faulkner's life as a human being and as an artist. The time I refer to comprehends the years 1925, during the first six months of which Faulkner lived in New Orleans and was writing the "New Orleans Sketches" and his first novel, *Soldiers' Pay,* and 1926, during the summer of which he saw much of Helen Baird in Pascagoula, Mississippi, and in which time he wrote his second novel, *Mosquitoes.*

Though I believe that a literary critic's first concern is with the shape, meaning, and value of an author's fully developed works, he will find it also proper to consider the development of the young artist who created the later great works. Whatever value we may decide to place upon the minor works written during this period, such as *Mayday* and the sonnets that make up *Helen: A Courtship,* they do illuminate Faulkner's state of mind during this period. Moreover, so thoroughly was his hopeless love for Helen Baird involved in his writings in 1925-26 that the five letters to her, fragmentary though they are, manage to tell us a great deal. The proof of the importance I attach to these unique items in the Wisdom Collection is abundantly exhibited in pages 47-60 of my recently published *Toward Yoknapatawpha and Beyond.*

Helen, I should think, represents the effective end of Faulkner's attempt to write poetry. But if it reveals the termination of his poetic career, it also represents its summit, for some of the sonnets included are the most fully achieved poems that he ever wrote.

Helen and *Mayday* also represent Faulkner's most successful attempts to combine his early interest in line drawings, water-color painting, and calligraphy with literary craftsmanship. These two little volumes, so carefully lettered, illustrated, and handbound by the young artist, have great charm and are the best testimony of the seriousness with which Faulkner took the arts of the drawing pen and the painter's brush.

This material is indeed the highpoint of the Wisdom Collection and gives it its very special importance. I congratulate the Howard-Tilton Library for its having come into possession of very special documents relating to what I suppose most scholars and critics have come to regard as the South's greatest writer.

THE WILLIAM B. WISDOM COLLECTION OF WILLIAM FAULKNER

This descriptive catalogue of the William B. Wisdom Collection of William Faulkner describes the present holdings and also includes a checklist of Faulkner materials in other divisions of the Tulane Library, a note on the manuscripts and typescripts in the collection by Cleanth Brooks, and a personal memoir of William B. Wisdom as a Faulkner collector by Carvel Collins. When it is appropriate, items are keyed to Linton Massey's *"Man Working,"* *1919-1962: William Faulkner: A Catalogue of the William Faulkner Collections at the University of Virginia* (See 341.) with the symbol VC and to Joan St. C. Crane and E. H. Freudenberg's *Man Collecting* . . . (See Checklist, XI), an important and helpful exhibit catalogue, with the symbol MC.

The catalogue of the collection has two main divisions: works by Faulkner and works about Faulkner. Each division is organized into sections which are arranged alphabetically with the exception of the Faulkner letters, which are chronological. The first division has thirteen sections. Manuscripts and typescripts appear below subheadings of the appropriate sections. The second division includes six sections. In both divisions each item has a separate identifying number. The overall organization follows the pattern set by the Massey catalogue to allow for easy cross-reference.

Oil painting of William Faulkner by Helen Baird Lyman, 1955.

William Faulkner in his sailboat on Lake Sardis, Mississippi. Photograph by Lamarr Stephens, 1950.

William Faulkner at the helm of his sailboat on Lake Sardis, Mississippi. Photograph by Lamarr Stephens, 1950.

PART ONE: WORKS BY FAULKNER

I. NOVELS

1   *Absalom, Absalom!* New York: Random House, 1936.
     Limited edition, No. 37, and signed by the author. VC
     1. MC pp. 63-64.

2   *Absalom, Absalom!* New York: Random House, 1936.
     First edition, first printing. With dust jacket. VC 2.

3   *Absalom, Absalom!* London: Chatto & Windus, [1936].
     First edition, first British publication. VC 8.

4   *Absalom, Absalom!* [Tr. John Vandenbergh]. Hasselt:
     Uitgeverij Heideland, [1966]. With printed dust jacket.
     Chronology and genealogy.

5   *Absolone, Absolone!* [Tr. and afterward by Jiři Valja].
     Prague: Mladá Fronta, [1966]. With printed dust jack-
     et. Map and chronology.

6   *Absalom, Absalom.* Tr. Kai Kaila. Helsinki: Kustannu-
     sosakeyhtiö Tammi, [1967]. With pictorial dust jacket.
     Chronology, glossary, and map.

7   *Absalom, Absalom!* [Tr. G. Barklund]. Stockholm: Al-
     bert Bonniers Förlag, [1969]. Paper. Map and chro-
     nology.

8   *As I Lay Dying.* New York: Jonathan Cape and Harri-
     son Smith, [1930]. First edition, 1st state, 2 copies (dust
     jacket); 2nd state, 1 copy. VC 16. MC p. 41.

9   *Mentre morivo.* [Tr. Guilio de Angelis]. Italy: Arnoldo
     Mondadori, 1958. "I edizione." With printed dust
     jacket.

10   *The Sound and the Fury* and *As I Lay Dying*. New York: Modern Library, [1946]. First Modern Library edition. With dust jacket. VC 17. Two copies.

11   *A hang és a téboly/ Míg fekszem kiterítve*. Hungary: Európa Könyvkiadó, 1976. Biographical note by Geher István. Red-brown cover embossed in brown and gold on front and spine. List of characters, chronology.

12   *A Fable*. Uncorrected Proof. Random House: "December 1944/ Oxford-New York-Princeton/ November 1953." 310 p.

13   *A Fable*. [New York]: Random House, [1954]. Boxed. Limited edition, and signed by the author. Two copies: No. 51 and 576. VC 37. MC pp. 84-87.

14   *A Fable*. [New York]: Random House, [1954]. First edition, first printing. With dust jacket. VC 38. Two copies.

15   "Notes on a Horse Thief" [from *A Fable*]. *Vogue*, 124 (July 1954), 46-51, 101-107. VC 635. Headnote by Carvel Collins. Random House edition of novel appeared one month after this selection. Three copies.

16   *The Hamlet*. New York: Random House, 1940. Limited edition, No. 156, and signed by the author. VC 55. MC pp. 67-71.

17   *The Hamlet*. New York: Random House, 1940. First edition, first printing. With dust jacket. VC 56.

18   *The Hamlet*. New York: Random House, [1964]. Third edition, first printing as part of the Snopes trilogy. Boxed. VC 60. Two copies.

19   *The Long Hot Summer: A Dramatic Book from the Four-Book Novel, The Hamlet*. [New York]: The New American Library, [1958]. Paper edition, first printing.

VC 61. Part of the text, "The Hound," appeared originally in *Harper's Magazine*. Includes photographs of
six scenes from the movie version. Two copies.

20   *Intruder in the Dust*. New York: Random House,
      [1948]. First edition, first printing. With dust jacket.
      VC 72. MC pp. 73-75. Two copies.

21   *Light in August*. [New York]: Harrison Smith & Robert
      Haas, [1932]. First edition, first printing. Three copies,
      two with dust jackets. VC 103. MC pp. 50-52.

22   *Mørk august*. Tr. Sigurd Hoel. Oslo: Gyldendal Norsk
      Forlag, 1951. Paper. VC 125.

23   *Forløsning i august*. Tr. Sven Møller Kristensen. Oslo:
      Gyldendals Tranebøger, 1964. Paper. VC 134.

24   *Svetloba v augustu*. Yugoslavia: Cankarjeva Založba v
      Ljubljani, 1966. Intro. by Janko Kos. Paper.

25   *Liekehtivä elokuu*. Helsinki: Kustannusosakeyhtiö Tam-
      mi, [1968]. With pictorial dust jacket.

26   *Augustové svetlo*. [Tr. Ján Vilikovský]. Bratislava:
      Tatran, 1969. With dust jacket.

27   *Luce d'agosto*. Tr. Elio Vittorini. Italy: Arnoldo Mon-
      dadori, "I edizione I capolavori della Medusa Maggio
      1970." Green cover embossed on front and spine in gold.

28   *The Mansion*. New York: Random House, [1959]. Lim-
      ited edition, No. 413, and signed by the author. VC
      139. MC pp. 96-99.

29   *The Mansion*. New York: Random House, [1959].
      First trade edition. With pictorial dust jacket. VC 141.
      Two copies.

30   *The Mansion.* New York: Random House, [1964]. "Third printing," first printing as part of the Snopes trilogy. Boxed. VC 142. Two copies.

31   "Mink Snopes," *Esquire,* 52, No. 6 (December 1959), 226-230, 247-264. An episode from *The Mansion.* VC 144. Two copies.

32   *Mosquitoes.* New York: Boni and Liveright, 1927. First edition, first printing. VC 154. MC pp. 32-34. Three copies.

      One copy inscribed as a gift from Oliver La Farge to W. P. Spratling, 1927.

      Copies two and three have dust jackets different from each other.

33   *Pylon.* New York: Harrison Smith and Robert Haas, 1935. Limited edition and signed by the author, facing p. [316]. Boxed. Two numbered copies: 103 and 234. VC 172. MC pp. 61-62.

34   *Pylon.* New York: Harrison Smith and Robert Haas, 1935. First edition, first printing. With printed dust jacket. VC 174. Two copies.

35   *Pylone.* [Tr. R. N. Raimbault and G. Louis-Rousselet]. [Paris]: Gallimard, [1946]. Paper edition, No. 768. VC 183.

36   *The Reivers: A Reminiscence.* New York: Random House, [1962]. Limited edition and signed by the author. Two numbered copies: 172 and 174. VC 192. MC pp. 100-101.

37   *The Reivers: A Reminiscence.* New York: Random House, [1962]. First edition, first printing. With dust jacket. VC 193. Four copies.

38   "The Education of Lucius Priest." *Esquire,* 57, No. 5 (May 1962), [109-116]. An episode from *The Reivers,* with drawings. VC 198. Four copies.

39   *Requiem for a Nun.* New York: Random House, [1951]. Limited edition and signed by the author. Two numbered copies: 276 and 593. VC 219. MC pp. 80-81.

40   *Requiem for a Nun.* New York: Random House, [1951]. First edition, first printing. With dust jacket. VC 220. Three copies.

41   *Requiem für eine Nonne.* [Tr. Robert Schnorr]. [Munich]: Deutscher Taschenbuch Verlag, [October 1964]. Paper. VC 233.

42   *Prize Stories of 1951: The O. Henry Awards.* Herschel Brickell, ed. Garden City, New York: Doubleday, 1951. First edition. With dust jacket. Includes "A Name for the City," an excerpt from *Requiem for a Nun.* See p. xvi and p. 98. VC 227.

43   Ford, Ruth, adaptor. *Requiem for a Nun: A Play from the Novel by William Faulkner* . . . . New York: Random House, [1959]. First edition, first printing. With dust jacket. Preface by Faulkner. VC 241. Two copies.

44   *Sanctuary.* New York: Jonathan Cape & Harrison Smith, [1931]. First edition, second printing. Two copies, one with dust jacket. VC 249. MC pp. 42-44.

45   *Sanctuary.* London: Chatto and Windus, 1931. First British edition, first printing. VC 264. Inscription: "Given to/ John Hampson Simpson/ by/ Charles Lahr/ December 1931."

46   *Sanctuary.* New York: Modern Library, [1932]. First Modern Library edition. VC 254. Three copies: one

with green cover and dust jacket, a second with green cover, and a third with red cover.

47   *Sanctuary.* New York: Modern Library, [c. 1932]. With dust jacket drawing dated " '40." VC 255.

48   *Sanctuary.* New York: Random House, [1958]. First edition reprint. With dust jacket. VC 260. Five copies.

49   *Die Freistatt.* [Tr. Herberth E. Herlitschka]. [West Berlin]: Ullstein Bücher, [1960]. Paper.

50   *Sartoris.* New York: Harcourt, Brace and Company, [1929]. First edition, first printing. With dust jacket. VC 289. MC pp. 35-36. Two copies. Inside rear flap of jacket contains advertisement for Ben Wasson's novel *The Devil Beats His Wife.*

51   *Sartoris.* New York: Random House, [1956]. First edition, reprint. With dust jacket. VC 292.

52   *Soldiers' Pay.* New York: Boni and Liveright, 1926. First edition, first printing of Faulkner's first novel. VC 304. MC pp. 29-30. Three copies: one with dust jacket, a second inscribed: "Carolyn Clark Wright/ From Grace/ May 1926." A third inscribed: "George B. Weaks" on title page and endpaper.

53   *Monnaie de singe.* Tr. Maxime Gaucher. Grenoble-Paris: B. Arthaud, [1948]. Paper. VC 312.

54   *The Sound and the Fury.* New York: Jonathan Cape and Harrison Smith, [1929]. First edition, first printing. VC 322. MC pp. 37-40. Three copies: One signed "William Faulkner/ 23 Aug. 1930" with added inscription, a second with dust jacket, and a third inscribed: "L. S. McGehee."

55   *Stormen och vreden.* [Tr. G. Barklund]. [Stockholm]: Bonniers, [1964]. Paper. VC 344.

56   *Kirk i bijes.* Zagreb, Yugoslavia: Naprijed, 1965. Introduction by Stjepan Krešić. Includes Faulkner's appendix. With dust jacket.

57   *Het Geraas en Gebral.* Tr. John Vandenbergh. Utrecht: A. W. Bruna & Zoon, [1965]. With Faulkner's glossary.

58   *Larmen og vreden.* Tr. Helge Simonsen. Oslo: Gyldendal Norsk Forlag, [1967]. Paper.

59   *Brϕlet og Vreden.* Tr. Knud Müller. Copenhagen: Gyldendals Bekkasinbϕger, [1968]. Paper. With Faulkner's appendix.

60   *Zgomotul și furia.* Tr. Mircea Ivănescu. Bucuresti: Univers, 1971. Paper. With Faulkner's glossary.

61   *A hang és a téboly.* Hungary: Európa Könyvkiadó, n.d. With dust jacket. Includes list of characters and Faulkner's glossary.

62   *The Town.* New York: Random House, [1957]. Limited edition, No. 148, and signed by the author. VC 346. MC pp. 94-95.

63   *The Town.* New York: Random House, [1957]. First edition, first printing. With pictorial dust jacket. VC 347. Two copies.

64   *The Town.* New York: Random House, [1964]. "Fourth printing," first printing as part of the Snopes trilogy. Boxed. VC 350. Two copies.

65   *The Saturday Evening Post Stories 1957.* New York: Random House, [1957]. With dust jacket. VC 352. Includes "The Waifs," an excerpt from *The Town.*

66   *The Unvanquished.* New York: Random House, [1938]. Limited edition, No. 77, and signed by the author. VC 364. MC p. 65.

67   *The Unvanquished*. New York: Random House, [1938]. First edition, first printing. With dust jacket. VC 365.

68   *The Unvanquished*. New York: The New American Library, [1959]. Foreword by Carvel Collins. Paper. VC 369. Two copies: one inscribed "To Bill [Wisdom]/ With Thanks!/ from Carvel [Collins]"; the second signed on title page by Carvel Collins.

69   *The Wild Palms*. New York: Random House, [1939]. Limited edition, No. 249, and signed by the author. VC 386. MC pp. 66-67.

70   *The Wild Palms*. New York: Random House, [1939]. First edition, first printing. With dust jacket. VC 388.

71   *The Wild Palms*. New York: The New American Library, [1948]. Reprint of first edition, "second printing, March, 1948." Paper. Pictorial cover.

72   *The Wild Palms* and *The Old Man* [Sic]. New York: The New American Library, [1954]. Paper. With pictorial cover.

73   *Wilde Palmen* und *Der Strom*. Zurich: Fretz & Wasmuth, [1957]. With dust jacket. VC 404.

74   *Yasei no jōnetsu*. Tokyo: Mikasa Shobō, 1951. With dust jacket. VC 409.

75   Foote, Horton. *Three Plays*. New York: Harcourt, Brace & World, Inc., [1962]. First edition. Paper. Includes adaptations of "Old Man" and "Tomorrow."

TYPESCRIPTS

76   From *Absalom, Absalom!* Original. Published in revised form in *American Mercury,* part of series titled "Works

[26]

in Progress." Corrections and deletions marked. 24p. See 77.

77   From *Absalom, Absalom!* Revised. Published in *American Mercury,* part of series titled "Works in Progress." With proofreader's marks. Stamped and numbered: American Mercury 234 31229 to 248 31229. 15p. See 76.

II.   SHORT STORIES

COLLECTIONS

78   *Big Woods.* New York: Random House, [1955]. First edition, first printing. With dust jacket VC 424. MC pp. 88-90. Two copies.

79   *Collected Stories of William Faulkner.* New York: Random House, [1950]. First edition, first printing. With printed dust jacket. VC 427. MC pp. 79-80. Two copies.

80   *The Collected Short Stories of William Faulkner.* Vol. I *Uncle Willy and Other Stories.* London: Chatto & Windus, 1958. Offset from *Collected Stories.* First edition, reprint. With dust jacket. VC 432. Two copies.

81   *Doctor Martino and Other Stories.* New York: Harrison Smith and Robert Haas, 1934. Limited edition, No. 94, and signed by the author. VC 437. MC pp. 59-60.

82   *Doctor Martino and Other Stories.* New York: Harrison Smith and Robert Haas, 1934. First edition, possibly second printing. Two copies, one with dust jacket. VC 438.

83   *The Faulkner Reader.* New York: Random House, [1954]. First appearance of the author's "Foreword."

First edition, first printing. With pictorial dust jacket. VC 443. Two copies.

84   *The Faulkner Reader.* New York: Modern Library, [1959]. First edition, reprint. "First Modern Library Giant Edition." With dust jacket. VC 444. Two copies.

85   *Faulkner's County: Tales of Yoknapatawpha County.* London: Chatto & Windus, 1955. First edition, first printing. With printed dust jacket. VC 446.

86   *Go Down, Moses, and Other Stories.* New York: Random House, [1942]. First edition, first printing. With dust jacket. VC 449. MC pp. 71-73.

87   *Scendi, Mosè.* [Tr. Edoardo Bizzarri]. Milan: Arnoldo Mondadori, 1947. "I Edizione." Paper. With leaflet advertising the book. VC 460.

88   *Das verworfene Erbe.* [Tr. Hermann Stresau]. [Hamburg]: Fischer Bücherei, "November 1964." Paper.

89   *Jealousy and Episode: Two Stories by William Faulkner.* Minneapolis: Faulkner Studies, 1955. Limited edition. Four copies. No. 147, 149, 150, 155. VC 463.

90   *Knight's Gambit.* New York: Random House, [1949]. First edition, first printing. With dust jacket. VC 464. MC pp. 75-77. Three copies.

91   *Mirrors of Chartres Street.* [Minneapolis: Faulkner Studies, 1953]. Limited edition, only printing. Two copies: No. 155 and 156. With dust jacket. VC 480. MC pp. 83-84.

92   *New Orleans Sketches.* Ed. Ichiro Nishizaki. Tokyo: Hokuseido, n.d. In English. Notes. Two copies. VC 481 for related information.

93   *New Orleans Sketches*. Ed. with Introd. by Carvel Collins. New Brunswick: Rutgers University Press, 1958. First American edition, first printing. With dust jacket. VC 484. Six copies: three copies signed on the title page by Carvel Collins.

94   *New Orleans Sketches*. Ed. with Introd. by Carvel Collins. London: Sidgwick and Jackson, [1959]. First American edition, British reprint. With dust jacket. VC 486. Signed on the title page by Carvel Collins.

95   *New Orleans Sketches*. Ed. with Introd. by Carvel Collins. New York: Grove Press, [1961]. First American edition, reprint. Paper. VC 485. Signed on the title page by Carvel Collins.

96   *New Orleans Sketches*. Ed. Carvel Collins. New York: Random House, [1968]. Second edition, first printing. Preface. Introduction. Blue boards with gold and orange embossing on front and spine. Off-white endpapers. Top edge red. With printed dust jacket. Additional essay included as an appendix: "Sherwood Anderson." Three copies: one inscribed: "For Bill Wisdom,/ in gratitude/for everything/Carvel"; a second signed on the title page by Carvel Collins; and a third signed on initial endpaper by William B. Wisdom with annotation there, on p. vi and p. 6 re Faulkner's use of the word *trun*.

97   *The Portable Faulkner*. Ed. Malcolm Cowley. New York: Viking, 1946. First edition, first printing. With dust jacket. VC 494.

98   *The Portable Faulkner*. Ed. Malcolm Cowley. New York: Viking, 1961. First edition, "SEVENTH PRINTING (X P)." Paper. VC 497.

99   *Selected Short Stories of William Faulkner*. New York: Modern Library, [1962]. First edition, "first printing." With printed dust jacket. VC 502.

100 *These 13.* New York: Jonathan Cape & Harrison Smith, [1931]. Limited edition, No. 42, and signed by the author. VC 506. MC p. 46.

101 *These 13.* New York: Jonathan Cape & Harrison Smith, [1931]. First edition, presumably second printing. With printed book jacket. VC 507.

INDIVIDUAL STORIES

102 "Afternoon of a Cow by Ernest V. Trueblood." *Furioso,* 2 (Summer 1947), 5-17. With "Notes on Mr. Faulkner," by R. W. [Reed Whitemore]. VC 518. A self-parody. Two copies.

103 "The Bear." *The College Omnibus.* Ed. Leonard F. Dean. New York: Harcourt, Brace and Company, 1951. VC 537. With study notes.

104 "An Error in Chemistry." *The Queen's Awards, 1946.* Ed. Ellery Queen [pseud.]. Boston: Little, Brown, 1946. VC 588.

105 "Gold Is Not Always." *Jubilee: One Hundred Years of the Atlantic.* Eds. Edward Weeks and Emily Flint. Boston: Little, Brown, [1957]. VC 600.

106 *Idyll in the Desert.* New York: Random House, 1931. Limited edition, No. 204, and signed by the author. Only edition, only printing. VC 611. MC p. 48.

107 *Mayday.* "This facsimile of *Mayday* was printed and handbound for the University of Notre Dame Press by the Stein Printing Company, Atlanta, Georgia in November, 1976." "Copyright 1976 by Jill Faulkner Summers." Edition limited to twenty-five presentation copies and one hundred and twenty-five numbered copies. This is a presentation copy. With a separately bound essay by

Carvel Collins, *Faulkner's "Mayday."* Notre Dame: University of Notre Dame Press, [1977]. Contains illustration from endpaper of *Mayday* on p. 27. Boxed. See 120.

108   *Miss Zilphia Gant.* [Dallas]: The Book Club of Texas, 1932. Limited edition, No. 252. VC 621. MC p. 55.

109   "Mr. Acarius." *The Saturday Evening Post.* October 9, 1965, pp. 26-31. Introd. by Joseph Blotner. Two copies.

110   "Mr. Acarius." *The Best American Short Stories, 1966.* Eds. Martha Foley and David Burnett. Boston: Houghton Mifflin Company, 1966.

111   "My Grandmother Millard and General Bedford Forrest and the Battle of Harrykin Creek." *Story: The Fiction of the Forties.* Eds. Whit Burnett and Hallie Burnett. New York: Dutton, 1949. VC 630.

112   *Notes on a Horsethief.* Greenville, Mississippi: The Levee Press, 1950. Limited edition and signed by the author. Seven copies: No. 5, 74, 75, 76, 130, 342, 343. VC 633.

113   "Once Aboard the Lugger." *Contempo,* 1, No. 17 (February 1, 1932), 1, 4. VC 643. Rpt. in *Uncollected Stories.* Reflects Faulkner's alleged bootlegging experiences in the Gulf. A complete issue by Faulkner. See 128.

114   "Pantaloon in Black." *Harper's Magazine,* No. 1085 (October 1940), 503-513. VC 644.

115   "Turn About." *The Saturday Evening Post Treasury.* New York: Simon and Schuster, [1954].

116   "Two Soldiers." *The Best Short Stories of World War II.* Ed. Charles A. Fenton. New York: Viking, 1957. VC 724.

MANUSCRIPTS AND TYPESCRIPTS

117   "Centaur in Brass." Original typescript. 24p. With corrections. Appeared in *American Mercury,* 35, No. 98 (February 1932). Reprinted in *Collected Stories.* Part of the Snopes material incorporated into *The Town.* Stamped and numbered: 166 17411 to 189 17411.

118   "Golden Land." Original typescript. 34p. With light corrections. Appeared in *American Mercury,* 35, No. 137 (May 1935). Stamped and numbered: 27064 1 to 27064 34. Story of young man from Nebraska now in Beverly Hills, California. Interesting use of typography —headlines and telegrams. Reprinted in *Collected Stories.*

119   "Hair." Original typescript. 21p. With corrections. Appeared in *American Mercury,* 23, No. 89 (May 1931). Stamped and numbered: 15485 282 to 15485 302. One of the three stories Faulkner liked best in *These 13,* in which it is reprinted. The story is associated with *Sanctuary* and is set in Jefferson. A central character, Maxey the barber, appears in *Light in August.*

120   *Mayday.* Handbound, written, and illustrated by the author. "OXFORD, MISSISSIPPI, 27 JANUARY, 1926." 43p. Illustrations: two black-and-white drawings as endpapers, three full-page watercolors, five emblazoned initial letters, and a heraldic device at conclusion. Cloth-backed, papers-over-boards cover in marble-like pattern of blue, green, and yellow. Paper label affixed to front cover. Subtitles on each page. The printing is affected with the *v* for *u* and the *s* in reverse position. Dedicated "to thee/ O wise and lovely" [Helen Baird]. A narrative of Arthurian character with hero, visions, quest, love, and allegory. See 107.

121   "The Mirror of Chartres Street./No. 7: New Orleans." Original typescript. n.d. 9p. With editor's corrections

and changes. First appearance in *The Double Dealer.*
Rpt. in *New Orleans Sketches,* ed. Carvel Collins. Contains a descriptive catalogue of characters: a wealthy
Jew, a priest, Frankie and Johnny, a cobbler, a longshoreman, a cop, a beggar, an artist, Magdalen, and the
tourist. The sailor does not appear in this typescript.

122   "Pennsylvania Station." Original typescript. 22p. With
light corrections. Appeared in *American Mercury,* 31,
No. 122 (February 1934). Stamped and numbered:
23313 304 to 23313 325. Reprinted in *Collected Stories.*
Set in New York, the story has an interest in the building of a coffin and suggests *As I Lay Dying.*

123   "That Will Be Fine." Original typescript. 29p. With
corrections and deletions. Appeared in *American Mercury,* 35, No. 139 (July 1935). Stamped and numbered
27659 27 to 27659 55. Reprinted in *Collected Stories.*
Story set at a Christmas in Mottstown "up from Jefferson."

124   "Uncle Willy." Original typescript. 27p. With light
corrections and deletions. Appeared in *American Mercury,* 36, No. 124 (October 1935). Stamped and numbered: 28398 25 to 28398 51. Reprinted in *Collected
Stories.* Set in Jefferson-Memphis area, the story centers
on Willy, a morphine addict who finally manages to
fly—in his own plane.

CHILDREN'S STORY

125   "The Wishing Tree." *The Saturday Evening Post,* April
8, 1967, pp. 48-53, 57-63. First publication, Illustrated.
Two copies.

126   *The Wishing Tree.* New York: Random House, [1967].
Illustrations by Don Bolognese. 82p. Light green cloth

on boards. Embossed in gold on front and spine. Blue top edge. Blue endpapers. Limited edition of 500 copies of which this is No. 340. First edition. Boxed. See "Publisher's Note." MC pp. 101-103.

127   *The Wishing Tree.* New York: Random House, [1967]. Illustrated by Don Bolognese. 82p. Light blue cloth on boards. Spine embossed in gold. Yellow top edge. First edition, "First Printing." With printed dust jacket. See "Publisher's Note." MC p. 103. Three copies.

III.   VERSE

128   "Complete Issue by . . . ." *Contempo,* 1, No. 17 (February 1, 1932), 1-4. Published at Chapel Hill, North Carolina. Includes the following poems: "I Will Not Weep for Youth," "Knew I Love Once," "Twilight," "Visions in Spring," "Spring," "April," "To a Virgin," "Winter Is Gone," and "My Epitaph." Also a short story, "Once Aboard the Lugger." VC 750. See editorial note on Faulkner. See 113.

129   "Dying Gladiator." *The Double Dealer,* 7, No. 41-42 (January-February 1925), 85. VC 745. Two copies.

130   *Faulkner's University Pieces.* Compilation and introduction by Carvel Collins. Tokyo: Kenkyusha Limited, [1962]. With printed dust jacket. VC 768. Two copies: one inscribed "For Bill [Wisdom],/ in gratitude & friendship/ — Carvel [Collins]" and the second signed by Carvel Collins.

131   "The Faun." *The Double Dealer,* 7, No. 43 (April 1925), 148. Dedicated to H.L. VC 746.

132   "The Flowers That Died." *Contempo,* 3, No. 10 (June 25, 1933), 1. Faulkner listed on staff, p. 2.

133 *A Green Bough*. New York: Harrison Smith and Robert Haas, 1933. Limited edition, No. 174, and signed by the author. First edition, first printing. VC 755. MC pp. 56-58.

134 *A Green Bough*. New York: Harrison Smith and Robert Haas, 1933. First edition, first printing. With dust jacket. VC 756.

135 "I Will Not Weep for Youth," "My Epitaph," "To a Virgin," "Winter Is Gone," "Knew I Love Once," and "Twilight." *An Anthology of the Younger Poets*. Ed. Oliver Wells. Philadelphia: Centaur Press, 1932. VC 751. Three copies.

136 "The Lilacs." *The Double Dealer,* 7, No. 44 (June 1925), 185-187. Dedicated to A. and H., Royal Air Force, August 1925. VC 747. See 149.

137 *The Marble Faun*. Boston: The Four Seas Company, [1924]. Introduction by Phil Stone. First separate edition and printing. VC 743. MC pp. 27-28. Two copies.

138 *The Marble Faun* and *A Green Bough*. New York: Random House, [1965]. With printed dust packet. VC 744.

139 "Portrait." *The Double Dealer,* 3, No. 18 (June 1922), 337. VC 740. See "Notes on Contributors" inside front cover.

140 *Salmagundi*. Milwaukee: The Casanova Press, 1932. Limited edition, No. 290. VC 753. MC pp. 49-50. A selection of Faulkner's *Double Dealer* contributions and one poem by Hemingway.

141 *This Earth*. New York: Equinox, 1932. Only edition, only printing. Paper. VC 754.

142   "William Faulkner." *Mississippi Verse*. Ed. Alice James. Chapel Hill: University of North Carolina Press, 1934. VC 761. Five copies, four with dust jackets.

143   *William Faulkner: Early Prose and Poetry*. Compilation and Introduction by Carvel Collins. Boston: Little, Brown, [1962]. First edition, first printing. With printed dust jacket. With Faulkner sketches. VC 770. Seven copies: five signed on the title page by Carvel Collins.

144   *William Faulkner: Early Prose and Poetry*. Compilation and Introduction by Carvel Collins. Boston: Little, Brown, [1962]. "First edition." With Faulkner sketches. Paper. Two copies: signed on the title page by Carvel Collins.

145   *William Faulkner: Early Prose and Poetry*. Compilation and Introduction by Carvel Collins. London: Jonathan Cape, [1963]. With dust jacket. VC 771.

146   *William Faulkner: Proses, poésies et essais critiques de jeunesse*. Ed. Carvel Collins. Translation and Preface by Henri Thomas. Illustrations by Faulkner. [Paris]: Gallimard, [1966]. Paper. Pink printed cover with end flaps.

MANUSCRIPTS AND TYPESCRIPTS

147   [Behind the mask—a maiden's face]. Untitled holograph. Ten lines in pencil on lined paper. No date. No signature. Paper folder for poem reads "Poem/inside," followed by the first and second lines.

148   *Helen: A Courtship*. Handbound and written by the author. "Single manuscript impression/ Oxford-Mississippi—June 1926." 18*l*. Cloth-backed, papers-overboards cover in marble-like pattern of blue, red, purple, gold, and orange. Paper label affixed to front cover.

[36]

Title page distinguished by a fleur-de-lis. The printing is affected with the *v* for *u* and the *s* in reverse position. Dedicatory poem, "To Helen, Swimming" (Pascagoula, June 1925), followed by fifteen other poems, each being on the recto of an individual page: I "Bill" (Pascagoula, 1925); II [Beneath the apple tree Eve's tortured shape] (Pascagoula, June 1925); III [With laggard March, a faun whose stampings ring] (Pascagoula, June 1925); IV [Her unripe shallow breast is green among] (Pascagoula, June 1925); V "Proposal" (Pascagoula, June 1925); VI [My health? My health's a fevered loud distress] (Pascagoula, June 1925); VII [The Centaur takes the sun to skull his lyre] (Pascagoula, June 1925); VIII "Virginity" (Majorca, July 1925); IX [Goodbye, goodnight: goodnight were more than fair] (Genoa, August 1925); X [Ah, no, ah no: my sleep is mine, mine own] (Pavia, August 1925); XI [Let that sleep have no end which brings me waking] (Pavia, August 1925); XII [Let there be no farewell shaped between] (Lago Maggiore, August 1925); XIII [O I have heard the evening trumpeted] (Lago Maggiore, 1925); XIV [Somewhere is spring with green and simple gold] (Paris, September 1925); XV [Knew I love once? Was it love or grief] (Paris, September 1925).

149   "The Lilacs." Typescript. 3p. Sixty-eight lines. First printed in *The Double Dealer*. See 136. See also 358-9, note and letter by Julius Friend, the editor.

150   [The meadow, the shadowy water]. Xerox copy of holograph. Eighteen-line fragment. Given to Bell I. Wiley by Phil Stone, c.1941.

151   [She is like a tower of warm ivory]. Untitled holograph. Nine lines on lined paper. No date. Signed "William Falkner." Illustrated with an apparent self-caricature. Paper folder for poem reads "Poem/inside" followed by the first line.

152   [You have seen music, heard]. Untitled typescript. Six lines. No date. No signature. Possibly related to Helen Baird.

IV.   PLAYS

152a   *Marionettes: A Play in One Act.* Oxford, Mississippi: Yoknapatawpha Press, "October 1975." Facsimile of the hand-lettered, illustrated, and bound MS. No. 63 of a limited edition of 510 copies. Boxed with pamphlet *A Memory of Marionettes* by Ben Wasson. Of the six original copies, one is in the University of Virginia Library, two are in the library of the University of Texas at Austin, and one is in the possession of Howard Duvall of Oxford, Mississippi.

152b   *The Marionettes.* Charlottesville: "Published for The Bibliographical Society of the University of Virginia by the University Press of Virginia," 1977. Introd. and textual apparatus by Noel Polk. "The facsimile . . . is of the Virginia copy of the play, which is slightly enlarged." Appendices include an introduction, descriptions of the manuscripts, historical collation, and alterations in the manuscripts. Illustrations from the Texas and Virginia copies.

V.   ESSAYS AND ARTICLES

153   "The Duty to Be Free." *The Freeman,* 3, No. 9 (January 26, 1953), 304-306. On "the sturdy virtue of responsibility."

154   "A Guest's Impression of New England." *New England Journeys. Number 2. Ford Times Special Edition.* [Dearborn, Michigan: Ford Motor Company, 1954]. VC 780. On the individuality of the people.

155   "A Guest's Impression of New England." *The Ford Times Guide to Travel in USA*. New York: Golden Press, [1962]. Reprint of article in *New England Journeys*. VC 781. See 154.

156   "Kentucky: May: Saturday." *Sports Illustrated*, 2, No. 20 (May 16, 1955), 22-24, 26. VC 784. Three copies. On the ambiance of the Kentucky Derby.

157   "Mississippi." *Holiday*, 15, No. 4 (April 1954), 34-47. VC 776. Two copies. A personal view, with photographs.

158   "New Orleans" [Original title, "The Mirror of Chartres Street No. 7: New Orleans"]. *The Double Dealer*, 7, No. 41-42 (January-February 1925), 102-107. See "Notes on Contributors." Three copies: two in poor condition. See 121.

159   "On Fear: The South in Labor." *Harper's Magazine*, 212, No. 1273 (June 1956), 29-34. VC 794. Three copies. Argues for blacks' involvement in the "American Dream."

160   "Sepulture South: Gaslight." *Harper's Bazaar*, 88, No. 2917 (December 1954), 84, 140-141. VC 782. Three copies. A personal memoir and reflection on mortality. With a Walker Evans photograph.

161   Spratling, William P. and William Faulkner. *Sherwood Anderson & Other Famous Creoles: A Gallery of Contemporary New Orleans*. New Orleans: The Pelican Bookshop Press, 1926. Limited edition, no copy number. VC 773. MC pp. 31-32. Three copies: the first inscribed: "and to my landlords,/ Marc & Lou [Antony] /W. Spratling/ New Orleans—Dec, 1926"; signed below their caricatures are Sherwood Anderson with a note, W. C. Odiorne, Moise Goldstein, Marc Antony, Conrad Albrizio, Keith Temple, Louis Andrews Fischer,

Lyle Saxon, Harold M. Levy, Caroline Wogan Durieux "(1968)," Genevieve Pitot, and Louis Gilmore.

Second copy: Limited edition, No. 188, and signed by Spratling. Without the multi-color special design of Spratling. Inscription: "and to Esther Dupuy . . . . New Orleans/ Feby 14th 1927/ (To my Valentine/ W.S.)" Also Sherwood Anderson's caricature colored in yellow and blue.

Third copy: Limited edition, No. 197. Without the multicolor special design of Spratling. Signature of Flo Field below her caricature.

162 ————. "Sherwood Anderson & Other Famous Creoles," *The Texas Quarterly,* 9, No. 1 (Spring 1966), 41-96. A facsimile reprint of the original title by the Pelican Bookshop Press, "SECOND ISSUE 150 COPIES/ JANUARY 1927." Also includes William Spratling, "Chronicle of a Friendship: William Faulkner in New Orleans" and Robert David Duncan, "William Spratling's Mexican World." Two copies. See 161.

163 ————. *Sherwood Anderson and Other Famous Creoles.* Austin: University of Texas Press, [1967]. Reprint of *The Texas Quarterly* text. See 162. Green cloth-covered boards with stamped spine. Spratling drawing on front cover. With printed dust jacket. Includes the Spratling and Duncan essays. Two copies.

VI.   CRITICISM

164 "Folklore of the Air." Review of *Test Pilot* by Jimmy Collins. Original typescript. 6p. With corrections and deletions. Appeared in *American Mercury,* 36, No. 143 (November 1935). Stamped and numbered: 199 28714 to 204 28714. A mixed review praising one section for its strong fictional treatment and another for its poetic expression.

165   "On Criticism." *The Double Dealer,* 7, No. 41-42 (January-February 1925), 83-84. VC 798. Attacks American critics for their "blindness" and unprofitable criticism. See 158.

166   "Verse Old and Nascent: A Pilgrimage." *The Double Dealer,* 7, No. 43 (April 1925), 129-131. VC 799. Acknowledges his debt to Swinburne and Housman and calls for a poet of the modern age. Note that "Books Received" lists Faulkner's *The Marble Faun.*

VII.   PUBLIC ADDRESSES

167   "American Segregation and the World Crisis." *The Segregation Decisions.* Atlanta: Southern Regional Council, 1956. Foreword by Bell I. Wiley, whose signature appears on the title page. VC 843.

168   ". . . 'Never Be Afraid': An Address . . . ." *The Oxford Eagle,* 83, No. 28 (May 31, 1951), 1. With article by Phil Mullen, pp. 1, 8. Two copies. See 169.

169   " 'Never Be Afraid.' " *Harvard Advocate,* 135, No. 2 (November 1951), 7. See Foreword, 6. VC 830. Four copies. Special Faulkner issue with essays on his works by major critics.

170   "Presentation to John Dos Passos of The Gold Medal for Fiction." *Proceedings of the American Academy of Arts and Letters.* Second series, No. 8, New York, 1958. VC 847. p. 192.

171   *William Faulkner's Speech of Acceptance upon the award of the Nobel Prize for Literature, delivered in Stockholm on the tenth of December, nineteen hundred fifty.* New York: Spiral Press, 1951. First separate edition, first printing. VC 811. Two copies.

172   *William Faulkner's Speech of Acceptance upon the award of the Nobel Prize* . . . . New York: Spiral Press, 1951. First separate edition, second printing. VC 812.

173   *William Faulkner's Speech of Acceptance upon the award of the Nobel Prize* . . . . New York: Spiral Press, 1951. First separate edition, third printing. VC 813.

174   *William Faulkner on Receiving the Nobel Price.* [New York]: Hunterdon Press, 1951. Second separate edition, first printing. VC 816.

175   William Faulkner's address on the occasion of his receiving on January 25 the National Book Award for his novel *A Fable,* in "Treasure Chest." *The New York Times Book Review,* February 6, 1955, pp. 2, 8, 24. VC 839. An advertisement with photograph of Faulkner, p. 23. Four copies.

176   William Faulkner's speech accepting the National Book Award in "The Book Industry Presents the Sixth National Book Awards." *Publishers' Weekly,* February 5, 1955, pp. 875-880. Includes photograph of advertisement of winning books.

177   "A Word to Virginians." *University of Virginia Magazine,* 2, No. 2 (Spring 1958), 11-14. VC 846. Issue includes second part of "William Faulkner on Dialect," 32-37. See 182.

VIII.   INTERVIEWS AND RELATED MATERIAL

178   Fant, Joseph L., III, and Robert Ashley, eds. *Faulkner at West Point.* New York: Random House, [1964]. With pictorial dust jacket. Photographs. VC 866. Three copies. Includes transcripts of several question and answer sessions and a "Reading from *The Reivers,*" among other material.

179   "Faulkner in Japan." *Esquire,* 50, No. 6 (December 1958), 139-142. VC 886.

180   *Faulkner on Truth and Freedom: Excerpts from Tape Recordings of Remarks Made by William Faulkner During His Recent Manila Visit.* [Manila]: The Philippine Writers' Association, n.d. Paper. Pictorial cover. VC 891. Personal and patriotic remarks made in 1955 on his tour for the State Department.

181   Gwynn, Frederick L. and Joseph L. Blotner, eds. *Faulkner in the University: Class Conferences at the University of Virginia, 1957-1958.* Charlottesville: University of Virginia Press, 1959. With printed dust jacket. VC 874. Three copies. Edited transcriptions of the classes.

182   ————. "William Faulkner on Dialect." *University of Virginia Magazine,* 2, No. 1 (Winter 1958), 7-13. VC 881. An interview. The second part is included in the next issue, pp. 32-37. See 177.

183   Jelliffe, Robert A., ed. *Faulkner at Nagano.* Tokyo: Kenkyusha, [1956]. With pictorial dust jacket. VC 885. Four copies.

184   Kimbrough, Edward and Betty Jane Holder. "The *Item* Interviews the Faulkners." *New Orleans Item,* October 29, 1951, pp. 1, 3, 4. Kimbrough, a novelist and *Item* staffer, interviews Faulkner; Miss Holder interviews Estelle Faulkner. Occasion of award from France. Photographs.

185   Meriwether, James B. and Michael Millgate, eds. *Lion in the Garden: Interviews with William Faulkner, 1926-1962.* New York: Random House, [1968]. With printed dust jacket. Four copies. Indexed for references to Faulkner's works, other authors, life and work, literature, places and people, and "The South and the Race Question." Does not include 184.

186   Rascoe, Lavon. "An Interview with William Faulkner." *Western Review*, 15, No. 4 (Summer 1951), 300-304. Questions asked Faulkner during his visit to a creative writing class at the University of Mississippi on April 16, 1947. VC 892. Important for his ranking of authors. A variation of "Classroom statements at the University of Mississippi" in 185.

187   Stein, Jean. "William Faulkner" in *Writers at Work*. Ed. Malcolm Cowley. New York: Viking Press, 1958. See pp. 120-141. VC 895. Two copies. With a "self-portrait" by Faulkner, a reproduction of the first manuscript page of *As I Lay Dying*, and a biographical note. Especially illuminating, this interview took place in New York in early 1956.

IX.   LETTERS

INTENDED FOR PUBLICATION

188   To the Editor. *The Commercial Appeal* [Memphis], March 20, 1955, Section 5, p. 3. VC 919. Two copies. On civil rights and Mississippi schools.

189   To the Editor. *The Commercial Appeal* [Memphis], March 27, 1955, Section 5, p. 3. Letters in response to Faulkner's letter of March 20, 1955. See 188. Included here for continuity.

190   To the Editor. *The Commercial Appeal* [Memphis], April 3, 1955, Section 5, p. 3. VC 921. Faulkner responds to the Neill, Martin, and Womack letters of March 20, 1955. See 189.

191   To the Editor. *The Commercial Appeal* [Memphis], April 10, 1955, Section 5, p. 3. VC 922. Faulkner responds to Murphy's letter of April 3, 1955. Includes other letters on the controversy.

192   To the Editor. *The Commercial Appeal* [Memphis],
        April 17, 1955, Section 5, p. 3. VC 923. Faulkner re-
        sponds to "student" letter of April 10, 1955. Includes
        among other letters on the controversy one signed
        "Mississippi Teacher."

193   To the Editor. *Life,* 40, No. 13 (March 26, 1956), 19.
        VC 929. Responds to reactions to his "Letter to the
        North" in *Life.* Other letters re Faulkner included here.

194   To the Editor. *Time,* April 23, 1956, p. 12. VC 931.
        Re a misquote on the segregation issue.

195   To the Editor. *The Commercial Appeal* [Memphis],
        September 15, 1957, Section 5, p. 3. VC 935. A warn-
        ing on the effects of continued resistance to integration.

196   "A Faulkner Letter" to David Kirk. *Crimson White,*
        [University of Alabama], 62, No. 27 (June 9, 1963), 1,
        3. Original letter, dated "8 March 1956," answers the
        question of what a student can do in order best to meet
        the desegregation problem. Included here for his prob-
        able intention that his views be widely spread.

NOT INTENDED FOR PUBLICATION

197   To Helen Baird. Typed. No date, "Monday." Signed,
        "Bill." Mentions May 16th. Indicates an enclosure,
        possibly a poem. Written from Oxford probably.

198   To Helen Baird. Typed. No date. Signed, "Bill." A
        cryptic note in script. Includes a description of Helen
        Baird.

199   To Helen Baird. In his script. No date, "Wednesday."
        Signed, "Bill." From Beverly Hills, California. Refers
        disparagingly to "these jobs"—probably the movie work.

200   To Helen Baird. In his script. No date, "broke since Jan 1." Unsigned. Sees a prolific writing period coming similar to that in Pascagoula.

201   To Helen Baird. In his script. No date. Signed, "Bill." Indicates location of "odds and ends of stories and notes." Comments that he finished a novel after three months' work and that he is contemplating other writing projects.

202   To Mrs. B. I. Wiley. Xerox copy. Dated Tuesday, [June 23, 1942]. Comments on the war, his attempts to enlist, and the genealogy of the McCaslins in *Go Down, Moses*.

203   Malcolm Cowley. *The Faulkner-Cowley File: Letters and Memories, 1944-1962*. New York: Viking Press, [1966]. First edition. With pictorial dust jacket. Four copies. Correspondence reflecting Faulkner's works and the process of his popular and critical discovery.

204   *A Keepsake for the Occasion of a Lecture: William Faulkner-Man Working 1897-1962 by Linton R. Massey*. San Francisco: Gleeson Library Associates of the University of San Francisco, January 21, 1968. Letter to Ben Wasson re the birth of Faulkner's daughter Jill and the use of colored inks in *The Sound and the Fury*.

X.   COLLECTED WORKS

205   *Essays, Speeches, and Public Letters*. Ed. James B. Meriwether. New York: Random House, [1965]. First edition. Blue cloth-covered boards with front and spine embossed in red and gold. Top edge, red. Grey endpapers. With printed dust jacket. Five copies. "Includes the text of all Faulkner's mature articles, speeches, book reviews, introductions to books, and letters intended for publication." Texts are authoritative and documented.

206   *Jefferson, Mississippi.* Edited and with an introduction by Michel Mohrt. [Paris: Le Club du meilleur livre, 1956]. Number 2643 of 5500. VC 1006. In French.

XI.   RECORDINGS BY FAULKNER

207   Reading from *Light in August.* Reel tape. At National Broadcasting Company, New York, on April 27, 1956. From the Modern Library edition, pp. 3-8, 421-430. Completed to p. 432 on 208. Arranger: Carvel Collins.

207a   Reading from *Light in August* and *The Bear.* Reel tape. At National Broadcasting Company, New York, on April 27, 1956. *Light in August* from the Modern Library edition (completes Hightower passage), pp. 430-432. See 207. *The Bear* from *Six Great Modern Short Novels,* Dell, pp. 444-448, 339-343. Arranger: Carvel Collins.

208   "William Faulkner reads The Nobel Prize Acceptance Speech and Selections from *As I Lay Dying, A Fable,* [and] *The Old Man.*" Caedmon Series of Literary Records, TC 1035.

XII.   DRAWINGS

209   *Ole Miss.* The Yearbook of the University of Mississippi. Vol. 25 (1920-1921). Drawings on pp. 129, 131, 137, 214-215. Note "Falkner" listed as a contributing editor, p. 94, and the poem by Wasson, p. 153.

210   *The Scream,* 1, No. 25 (May 1925), 11, 14. Published by the University of Mississippi. Two cartoon drawings with two-line captions. Faulkner listed on the art staff, p. 6.

XIII. MISCELLANEOUS ITEMS NOT OTHERWISE CATALOGUED

211 Farmer-District Cooperative Agreement, 270 B FP. Xerox copy. Revised. Dated, "6 Oct 1961." Signed, "William Faulkner." See related Price and Wisdom correspondence and "Plain Farmer" article in *The Clarion-Ledger* [Jackson, Miss.], 364, 367, 311.

212 "The Left Hand of God." Final screenplay. Mimeograph. July 18, 1952. Revised. 140p. Printed on one side. Copy number 25.

213 Marginal note on poem clipped from a magazine. No date. "How are you? Bill."

214 Recipe for curing meat. Xerox copy of typescript. Given to Mrs. Bell I. Wiley, 1941.

PART TWO: WORKS ABOUT FAULKNER

XIV. CRITICISM AND COMMENTARY

215   Adams, Richard P. "The Apprenticeship of William Faulkner." *Tulane Studies in English,* 12 (1962), 113-156. VC 1032. Jackson Bryer in *Sixteen Modern American Authors* states that this essay "is more significant and useful than most book-length studies of Faulkner."

216   ———. *Faulkner: Myth and Motion.* Princeton, New Jersey: Princeton University Press, 1968. Two copies: one inscribed "To Tess Crager/ Thanks and/ best wishes/ Dick [Adams]."

217   Backman, Melvin. *Faulkner: The Major Years. A Critical Study.* Bloomington and London: Indiana University Press, [1966].

218   Basso, Hamilton. "William Faulkner: Man and Writer." A Special Section. *Saturday Review,* July 28, 1962, pp. 11-26. VC 1103. Includes Lenore Marshall, "The Power of Words" and other articles by and about Faulkner. Illustrated.

219   Beck, Warren. *Man in Motion: Faulkner's Trilogy.* Madison: University of Wisconsin Press, 1961. VC 1116.

220   ———. *Man in Motion: Faulkner's Trilogy.* Madison: University of Wisconsin Press, 1961. Paper edition.

221   Blotner, Joseph. "The Regional Can Be Universal." A review of Martin J. Dain's *Faulkner's County: Yoknapatawpha. The New York Times Book Review,* October 25, 1964, p. 55. VC 1372. With photograph.

222   ———. Review of James B. Meriwether and Michael Millgate's *Lion in the Garden: Interviews with William Faulkner, 1926-1962. The New York Times Book Review,* June 30, 1968, p. 8.

223   ———. *William Faulkner's Library: A Catalogue.* Charlottesville: University of Virginia, [1964]. VC 1147. With an introduction. Lists American, English, European, and Eastern authors. Four copies: one inscribed "For/ William Wisdom/ with many thanks/ Joseph Blotner/ 2 Feb 1965."

224   ———. "William Faulkner's Name Was in the Books He Loved Best." *The New York Times Book Review,* December 8, 1963, pp. 4, 5, 45. VC 1148. The books as a reflection of the man. Issue also includes Lawrance Thompson's review of Cleanth Brooks' *The Yoknapatawpha Country,* pp. 4, 44-45. With photographs.

225   Breit, Harvey. "Talk with Irving Howe." *The New York Times Book Review,* July 20, 1952, p. 12. On Howe's *William Faulkner: A Critical Study.*

226   Brooks, Cleanth. "Faulkner as a Poet." Essay. Xerox copy of typescript [April 29, 1969]. Published in the *Southern Literary Journal,* 1 (1968), 5-19. Indicates Faulkner's poetic debt to Swinburne, Housman, Verlaine, *et al.*

227   ———. "Faulkner's Treatment of the Racial Problem: Typical Examples." *American Studies in Scandinavia,* No. 2 (Winter 1969), 24-40. Text corrected by Brooks. A lecture, given at the Otnäs Conference in 1967, in which he applies the technique of "close reading."

228   ———. *The Hidden God: Studies in Hemingway, Faulkner, Yeats, Eliot, and Warren.* New Haven: Yale University Press, [1963]. VC 1212.

229 ———. *William Faulkner: The Yoknapatawpha Country*. New Haven: Yale University Press, 1963. VC 1206. Two copies: one inscribed "For William B. Wisdom/ with cordial regards/ Cleanth Brooks"; a second inscribed "For Bill,/ an original, perhaps the original/ Faulknerian/ Cordially,/ Cleanth."

230 ———. *William Faulkner: The Yoknapatawpha Country*. New Haven: Yale University Press, [1966]. Paper edition. Principal additions and corrections on pp. 391, 448. Inscribed: "For William B. Wisdom/ with the author's cordial regards/ Cleanth Brooks."

231 ———. *William Faulkner: Toward Yoknapatawpha and Beyond*. New Haven: Yale University Press, 1978. Use of material from the William B. Wisdom Collection of William Faulkner is acknowledged on pp. xiv, xvii-xviii, 47, 52, 346, 349. On early prose and poetry, *Soldiers' Pay, Mosquitoes, Pylon, The Wild Palms,* and *A Fable*. With appendices, notes, and index.

232 Campbell, Harry Modean and Ruel E. Foster. *William Faulkner: A Critical Appraisal*. Norman: University of Oklahoma Press, [1951]. VC 1252. Two copies.

233 Cantwell, Robert. "Faulkner's 'Popeye.' " *The Nation,* 186, No. 7 (February 15, 1958), 140-141, 148. VC 1262.

234 Collins, Carvel. "Authors Mostly Are for Reading." A review of Frederick L. Gwynn and Joseph L. Blotner's *Faulkner in the University: Class Conferences at the University of Virginia, 1957-58. The New York Times Book Review,* October 11, 1959, p. 24.

235 ———. "Faulkner's *Mayday*." Introduction to reprint of *Mayday*. [Notre Dame, Indiana]: University of Notre Dame Press, [1977]. 30p. See 107. Explores the Faulkner-Baird relationship and comments on Faulkner's

New Haven visits and his 1925 visit to Paris. Links *Mayday* with Cabell's fiction and suggests *Mayday* as a Freudian prototype of *The Sound and the Fury.*

236 ———. *The Interior Monologues of The Sound and the Fury.* Publications in the Humanities No. 6. Cambridge: Department of Humanities, Massachusetts Institute of Technology, 1954. VC 1322. A paper originally presented at the English Institute meeting in September 1952.

237 ———. *Other Voices.* Publications in the Humanities No. 18. Cambridge: Department of Humanities, Massachusetts Institute of Technology, 1956. Reprint from *The American Scholar* (Winter 1955-56).

238 ———. "War and Peace and Mr. Faulkner." Review of *A Fable. The New York Times Book Review,* August 1, 1954, pp. 1, 13. VC 1326. With photograph.

239 Coughlan, Robert. "The Private World of William Faulkner," Part I. *Life,* 35, No. 13 (September 28, 1953), 118-136. VC 2598. With photographs and illustrations. Faulkner, his family, environment, and Yoknapatawpha.

240 ———. "The Man Behind the Faulkner Myth," Part II. *Life,* 35, No. 14 (October 5, 1953), 55-68. VC 2598. With photographs. Faulkner in Oxford and New Orleans; the relationship of his life to his works.

241 ———. *The Private World of William Faulkner.* New York: Harper, [1954]. VC 2601. Three copies.

242 Cowley, Malcolm. "Flem Snopes Gets His Come-Uppance." Review of *The Mansion. The New York Times Book Review,* November 15, 1959, pp. 1, 18. Issue includes coverage of Faulkner abroad. Photographs.

243   ———. "A Fresh Look at Faulkner." *Saturday Review,* June 11, 1966, pp. 22-26. With photograph. On the sense of place.

244   Dain, Martin J. *Faulkner's County: Yoknapatawpha.* New York: Random House, [1964]. VC 1371. Photographs with text. Three copies.

245   Downer, Alan S., ed. *English Institute Essays, 1952.* New York: Columbia University Press, 1954. VC 1406. Two copies: one inscribed "For Bill Wisdom/—Carvel Collins."

246   Driver, Tom F. "Faulkner's Faith Within Corruption." Review of *Requiem for a Nun* at the John Golden Theatre. *The New Republic,* March 9, 1959, p. 22. Sees the play as ineffective in its appeal "to those of lofty and lecherous mind."

247   Ellmann, Richard. "Faulkner as 'The Count.'" *Dimension.* The *Daily Northwestern* Magazine Supplement, 83, No. 112 (May 27, 1963), 3-4.

248   Everett, Walter K. *Faulkner's Art and Characters.* Woodbury, New York: Barron's Educational Series, [1969]. Includes dictionary of characters. Two copies.

249   *Faulkner: Three Studies.* Special Issue of *The Emporia State Research Studies,* 11, No. 1 (September 1962). VC 1401. Part I includes: Robert L. Dorsch, "An Interpretation of the Central Themes in the Work of William Faulkner"; Dorothy D. Greer, "Dilsey and Lucas: Faulkner's Use of the Negro as a Gauge of Moral Character." Three copies.

250   Ford, Margaret P. and Suzanne Kincaid. *Who's Who in Faulkner.* Baton Rouge: Louisiana State University Press, [1963]. Dictionary of characters with genealogical tables. VC 1474. Three copies.

251   Hicks, Granville. "Building Blocks of a Gentleman."
        Review of *The Reivers*. *Saturday Review,* June 2, 1962,
        p. 27. VC 1619. Not major Faulkner but very good
        minor Faulkner. Cover portrait.

252   Highet, Gilbert. "The New Books: Sound and Fury."
        Review essay of *A Fable*. *Harper's Magazine,* Septem-
        ber 1954, pp. 98-105. VC 1628. Faulkner as a perplex-
        ing writer, but one with a vision; *A Fable* as a perplex-
        ing dream narrative more like a poem.

253   Hoffman, Frederick J. *William Faulkner*. Twayne's
        United States Authors Series, I. New York: Twayne
        Publishers, [1961]. VC 1640.

254   ———. *William Faulkner*. Twayne's United States Au-
        thors Series, I. New Haven: College and University
        Press, [1961]. Paper edition. VC 1641.

255   Hoffman, Frederick J. and Olga W. Vickery. *William
        Faulkner: Three Decades of Criticism*. New York: Har-
        court, Brace, & World, [1963]. Paper edition. VC 1645.
        Reprint of Michigan State University edition, 1960.

256   ———. *William Faulkner: Two Decades of Criticism*.
        [East Lansing]: Michigan State College Press, 1951.
        VC 1646.

257   Howe, Irving. "Faulkner's Enduring Power." Review of
        *The Faulkner Reader. The New York Times Book Re-
        view,* April 4, 1954, pp. 1, 22. VC 1681. Faulkner's
        works place him in the pastoral tradition.

258   ———. "Thirteen Who Mutinied: Faulkner's
        First World War." Review of *A Fable. The Reporter,*
        September 14, 1954, pp. 43-45. VC 1669.

259   ———. *William Faulkner: A Critical Study*. New York:
        Random House, [1952]. VC 1671.

260   [Judson, Horace, *et al.*] "The Curse and the Hope" [cover story]. *Time,* July 17, 1964, pp. 44-48. VC 1737. Four copies. On Faulkner's view of the South.

261   Kerr, Elizabeth. *Yoknapatawpha: Faulkner's "Little Postage Stamp of Native Soil."* New York: Fordham University Press, 1969.

262   Kirk, Robert W. with Marvin Klotz. *Faulkner's People: A Complete Guide and Index to Characters in the Fiction of William Faulkner.* Berkeley-Los Angeles: University of California Press, 1963. VC 1768. Two copies.

263   "Letters." *Time,* July 24, 1964, p. 9. Bennett Cerf, John Hess, *et al.* respond to the July 17, 1964, cover story on Faulkner.

264   Linscott, Robert N. "Faulkner Without Fanfare." *Esquire,* July 1963, pp. 36-38. VC 2637. View by an editor from Random House.

265   Malin, Irving. *William Faulkner, an Interpretation.* Stanford, Calif.: Stanford University Press, [1957]. VC 1894.

266   Massey, Linton R. "Notes on the Unrevised Galleys of Faulkner's *Sanctuary." Studies in Bibliography,* 8 (1965), 195-208. VC 1905.

267   Mayes, Martha. "Faulkner Juvenilia." *New Campus Writing, No. 2,* ed. Nolan Miller. New York: Putnam's [1957], 135-144. VC 1912. Contains poems and other material associated with Faulkner's years at the University of Mississippi.

268   Meriwether, James B. "Notes on the Textual History of *The Sound and the Fury.*" *Papers of the Bibliographical Society of America,* 56 (1962), 285-316. VC 1923. Inscribed: "For Bill Wisdom/ with the compliments/ of the author:/ James B. Meriwether/ 2/11/63."

269   ———. "The Text of Faulkner's Books: An Introduction and Some Notes." *Modern Fiction Studies,* 9 (Summer 1963), 159-170. VC 1929. Inscribed: "For Bill Wisdom/ with the compliments of/ the author."

270   Millgate, Michael. *The Achievement of William Faulkner.* New York: Random House, [1966]. Two copies.

271   ———. *William Faulkner.* New York: Grove Press, [1961]. Paper. Two copies: one inscribed.

272   O'Connor, William Van. *The Tangled Fire of William Faulkner.* Minneapolis: University of Minnesota Press, [1954]. VC 2029. Two copies.

273   ———. *William Faulkner.* University of Minnesota Pamphlets on American Writers, No. 3. Minneapolis: University of Minnesota Press, [1959]. Two copies.

274   ———. *William Faulkner.* University of Minnesota Pamphlets on American Writers, No. 3. Minneapolis: University of Minnesota Press, "second printing 1960."

275   Pearson, Norman Holmes. "Faulkner's Three 'Evening Suns.' " *Yale University Library Gazette,* 29 (October 1954), 61-70. VC 2056. With reproduction of part of MS. on p. 62. Two copies.

276   Review of *Mirrors of Chartres Street. The Times-Picayune,* n.d. A commentary on the collected sketches which originally appeared in the reviewing newspaper.

277   Rubin, Louis D., Jr. *The Faraway Country: Writers of the Modern South.* Seattle: University of Washington Press, 1963. VC 2170. Chapter 3 on Faulkner and references throughout. Two copies.

278   Runyan, Harry. *A Faulkner Glossary.* New York: Citadel Press, [1964]. VC 2178. A guide to titles, characters, and places. With biographical, genealogical, and bibliographical appendices. Three copies.

279   Scott, Evelyn. *On William Faulkner's "The Sound and the Fury."* [New York: Jonathan Cape and Harrison Smith, Inc., c.1929]. Paper 10p. "The edition is limited to 1,000 copies." VC 2209. Sees the novel as a tragedy.

280   Slatoff, Walter J. *Quest for Failure: A Study of William Faulkner.* Ithaca, New York: Cornell University Press, [1961].

281   Smith, Harrison. "Purification by Sacrifice." Review of *Requiem for a Nun. Saturday Review,* September 29, 1951, p. 12. VC 2256. With annotations by William B. Wisdom.

282   Swiggart, Peter. *The Art of Faulkner's Novels.* Austin: University of Texas Press, [1962]. VC 2323. Two copies.

283   Thomson, James. "Warren Cites Faulkner as Nation's Top Writer." *Yale Daily News,* March 1, 1951, pp. 1, 6. Account of Robert Penn Warren's Bergen Lecture, "The South of William Faulkner."

284   Tuck, Dorothy. *Crowell's Handbook of Faulkner.* Advisory ed. Lewis Leary. New York: Thomas Y. Crowell, [1964]. VC 2370. Includes a biography and a dictionary of characters.

285   Vickery, Olga W. *The Novels of William Faulkner: A Critical Interpretation*. [Baton Rouge]: Louisiana State University Press, [1959]. VC 2391. Three copies.

286   Volpe, Edmond L. *A Reader's Guide to William Faulkner*. New York: Farrar, Straus, [1964]. A reference work for characters, themes, structure, style, and chronology.

287   Waggoner, Hyatt H. *William Faulkner: From Jefferson to the World*. [Lexington]: University of Kentucky Press [1959]. VC 2406. Two copies.

288   Warren, Robert Penn, ed. *Faulkner: A Collection of Critical Essays*. Englewood Cliffs, New Jersey: Prentice-Hall, [1966]. Essays by the editor, O'Donnell, Cowley, Aiken, Beck, Magny, Pouillon, Sartre, Millgate, Thompson, Blöcker, Vickery, Kubie, Kazin, Longley, Waggoner, Brooks, Lewis, Wilson, Hardwick, Lytle, Pritchett, and Podhoretz. Notes by Malraux, Tate, and Camus among others.

289   Warren, Robert Penn. "William Faulkner and His South." Mimeograph. The First Peters Rushton Seminar in Contemporary Prose and Poetry and the sixteenth in the series sponsored by the Schools of English, University of Virginia, 13 March 1951. 15p. VC 2426. Emphasizes "The great fact about Faulkner's work: he is concerned with good and evil, with the characteristically human."

XV.   BIOGRAPHICAL, ANECDOTAL, AND TOPICAL MATERIAL

290   Accounts of Faulkner's death. *The Commercial Appeal* [Memphis], July 7, 1962, pp. 1, 13. With photographs.

291   Anderson, Elizabeth and Gerald R. Kelly. *Miss Elizabeth: A Memoir*. Boston: Little, Brown, [1969]. Discusses Faulkner in New Orleans and *Mosquitoes*.

292   Anderson, Sherwood. *Letters of Sherwood Anderson*. Eds. Howard Mumford Jones and Walter B. Rideout. Boston: Little, Brown, [1953]. Letter to Faulkner, p. 162. References to Faulkner on pp. 145, 146, 154, 155, 162, 252, 310, 314, 339, 393.

293   Blotner, Joseph. *Faulkner: A Biography*. 2 Vols. New York: Random House, [1974]. Comprehensive treatment with notes, chronology, genealogy, and index. Illustrations.

293a   ———. "William Faulkner, Roving Ambassador." *International Educational and Cultural Exchange* (Summer 1966), 1-22. Accounts of Faulkner's travels for the State Department. Three copies.

294   Cowley, Malcolm. "The Solitude of William Faulkner." *The Atlantic*, 217, No. 6 (June 1966), 97-98, 101-106, 108-115. Includes texts of several Faulkner letters.

295   Cullen, John B. and Floyd C. Watkins. *Old Times in the Faulkner Country*. Chapel Hill: University of North Carolina Press, [1961]. VC 2604. Recollections of a fellow townsman of Faulkner's life. Three copies.

296   Falkner, Murry C. *The Falkners of Mississippi: A Memoir*. Baton Rouge: Louisiana State University Press, [1967].

296a   Faulkner, Estelle. Letter to Mary Vic [Mills]. Autograph. [c.1919]. Refers to an injury and a trip to Memphis. No mentiton of Faulkner.

296b   ———. Letter to Mary Vic [Mills]. Autograph. [c.1919]. Mentions visit of Bill Langston. No mention of Faulkner.

297   Faulkner, John. *My Brother Bill: An Affectionate Reminiscence*. New York: Trident Press, 1963. VC 2609. Portrays Faulkner as a boy. Two copies.

298   Faulkner Country Souvenir Edition. *The Oxford Eagle,* 108, No. 191 (August 6, 1976). Contains reprints of photographs and articles by and about Faulkner in addition to newer accounts.

299   "He Will Prevail." *Time,* July 13, 1962, pp. 85-86. VC 2686. A tribute to Faulkner's life and works.

300   Hicks, Granville. "The Public and Private Faulkner," *Saturday Review,* July 30, 1966, pp. 27-28. Critical of Faulkner's attitude toward privacy.

301   Keith, Don Lee. "Faulkner in New Orleans." *The Delta Review,* 6, No. 4 (May 1969), 46-49. Reminiscences by Faulkner's neighbors in the French Quarter. With drawing of Faulkner based on the Paris photograph.

302   Longstreet, Stephen. "My Friend, William Faulkner." *Cavalier,* 15, No. 142 (April 1965), 58-61. Faulkner in Hollywood. With drawings. See 303.

303   ————. "My Friend William Faulkner: Part II." *Cavalier,* 15, No. 143 (May 1965), 50-52, 85-86.

304   Meek, Ed. "Spring Workout." *Mississippi Magazine,* Spring 1962, pp. 12-13. Photographs with text. Faulkner cover photograph.

305   Memorial announcement. Printed in black letters on single sheet: "In Memory/of/William Faulkner/This Business Will Be [script]/Closed/From 2:00 To 2:15 P.M./Today, July 7, 1962."

306   Meriwether, James B. Review of John Faulkner's *My Brother Bill. The Houston Post,* September 15, 1963, Sec. 5, p. 8. Sees only anecdotal value and calls for a biography of Faulkner.

307   *The Osceola Times* [Osceola, Arkansas], 96, No. 51 (December 22, 1966), Sec. 3. The 8p special section on Faulkner includes "Never Be Afraid" and the "Nobel Award Acceptance Address." The major article is by Phil Mullen, the present editor, who had been Associate Editor of *The Oxford Eagle* from 1933 to 1951. Many photographs. Six copies.

308   *Oxford Mississippi: A Presentation of Essential Civic and Industrial Data.* Mimeograph and print. c.1952. 5p with appendix. Faulkner cited on p. 1 for the Nobel Prize and the French Legion of Honor. See J. W. Riever's letter to William B. Wisdom, 365.

309   "People." *Time,* February 7, 1955, p. 30. Faulkner's famous comment on his contemporaries, a follow-up to his statement about Hemingway's "cowardice."

310   Phelps, Robert and Peter Deane. *The Literary Life: A Scrapbook Almanac of the Anglo-American Literary Scene from 1900 to 1950.* New York: Farrar, Straus, and Giroux, 1968. References to Faulkner.

311   " 'Plain Farmer'/W. Faulkner Was/More Than That," *The Clarion-Ledger* [Jackson, Mississippi], March 28, 1970, p. 3. Refers to the Faulkner farm plan presented to the University of Mississippi. With an anecdote about Faulkner as a farmer by Henry Butler of Oxford.

312   "The Postmaster." *The New Yorker,* November 21, 1970, p. 50. Includes the complete letter outlining the charges against Faulkner for his neglect of duties at the University of Mississippi Post Office.

313   Putney, Michael. "Yoknapatawpha's Mr. Bill," *The National Observer,* February 16, 1974, p. 22. Biographical review of an author and his town. Photograph.

314   Saporta, Marc. "Retour au pays de Faulkner." *L'Atlantique* [Review published by the French Line], Sum-

mer-Autumn 1971, No. 1. In English and French. Cover photograph of Faulkner; also others. Two copies.

315   Schevill, James. *Sherwood Anderson: His Life and Work*. [Denver]: University of Denver Press, [1951]. References to Faulkner on pp. 106, 159, 194, 195, 207, 220, 225-6, 323, 333, 352.

316   Sketch of William Faulkner [print]. c.1930. Signed "Ah." Identifying note indicates the recent publication of *As I Lay Dying*.

317   Spratling, William. *File on Spratling: An Autobiography*. Boston: Little, Brown, [1967]. Chapter 3 on New Orleans and Faulkner. Two copies.

318   "Tribute to William Faulkner." *Mississippi Library News*, 26, No. 3 (September 1962), 97-103. Includes the Goldsborough portrait; a selection from the graduation speech at his daughter's high school commencement; the Nobel Address; articles by Hugh Holman and Paul Flowers; and notes by the editor. Five copies.

319   Webb, James W. and A. Wigfall Green, eds. *William Faulkner of Oxford*. [Baton Rouge]: Louisiana State University Press, [1965]. VC 2440. Personal glimpses of Faulkner by his associates. Seven copies.

320   Wilde, Meta Carpenter and Orin Borstin. Advance uncorrected proofs of *A Loving Gentleman: The Love Story of William Faulkner and Meta Carpenter*. New York: Simon and Schuster, [1976]. 259p. Without photographs.

321   "William Faulkner Souvenir Edition." *The Oxford Eagle*, 97, No. 24 (April 22, 1965). On the occasion of the University of Mississippi's hosting the annual South-

ern Literary Festival. Contains approximately **forty-five** articles reprinted from the files. With **photographs.**

322   "William Faulkner to Speak at Commencement." *The Cosmotarian* [Pine Manor Junior College, Wellesley, Massachusetts], 4, No. 5 (May 29, 1953), 1. At Jill Faulkner's graduation.

XVI.   PHOTOGRAPHS AND PAINTING OF FAULKNER

323   Cofield, Jack. *William Faulkner: The Cofield Collection.* Oxford, Mississippi: Yoknapatawpha Press, [1978]. Limited edition, No. 50 of 150 numbered copies, 162 total. Photographs. Introd. by Carvel Collins.

324   A group of formal and informal photographs by Lamarr Stephens. Some taken in Rowan Oak, others on board the sailboat.

325   "Faulkner Photographs Given University by Phil Mullen." *The Clarion-Ledger* [Jackson, Miss.], November 23, 1966, p. 11. Story includes photograph with anecdotes of Mullen's experiences with Faulkner.

326   Photograph of William Faulkner. Inscribed on front: "Bill." Inscribed on back: "Aug. 1917/William Faulkner/Oxford, Miss."

327   Portrait of William Faulkner by Helen Baird Lyman. Oil, 20 x 16 inches. See p. 18 and Collins' essay.

XVII.   EPHEMERA AND MISCELLANEOUS MATERIAL

328   Announcement of *Idyll in the Desert*. Random House. December 15, [c.1931]. An edition of 400 copies.

329   Brown, Maud Morrow. "William C. Falkner, Man of Legends." *Georgia Review,* 10, No. 4 (Winter 1956), 421-439. VC 2805. Regarding Faulkner's grandfather.

330   Falkner, W. C. *The White Rose of Memphis: A Novel.* New York: G. W. Dillingham Co., [1881]. VC 2797. Book stamp of J. H. Cain on title page. Author is Faulkner's grandfather.

331   Photograph of Harris Riley, Victoria Oldham, and Jerry York. Front inscribed "University Drilling Ground/ August 1917." Back inscribed with names cited above.

332   "Requiem for a Nun." *John Golden Theatre Playbill: A Weekly Magazine for Theatregoers,* 3, No. 8 (February 23, 1959), No. 9 (March 2, 1959). Three and six copies respectively.

333   Program for *Requiem pour une nonne* [by] William Faulkner [and adapted by] Albert Camus. Mathurins Théâtre Marcel Herrand, 1956-1957 season. Commentary on Faulkner by Camus. Photographs of Faulkner and Camus. Selections of French criticism on *Requiem.*

334   *The Scream* [published by the University of Mississippi], 1, No. 1 (November 6, 1924). No mention of Faulkner.

335   *The Scream,* 1, No. 2 (December 1924). No mention of Faulkner.

336   *The Scream,* 1, No. 3 (February 1925). Faulkner listed on art staff, p. 6.

337   *The Scream,* 2, No. 4 (March 1925). Faulkner listed on art staff, p. 4.

338   *The Scream,* 1925-1926. Vol. 2, No. 1-8 (bound). In No. 1 John Falkner is listed on art staff; drawings included. No. 3 and No. 6 also contain his drawings. The

cover of the volume is inscribed "George Healy, Jr./
Editor—The Scream—'25-'26."

339   Stone, Phil. Xerox copy of letter, dated November 5,
        1924, to the Four Seas Company and copies of three
        lists, relating to the publication of *The Marble Faun.*

XVIII. BIBLIOGRAPHIES AND CATALOGUES AND PROGRAMS OF EXHIBITIONS

339a   Boozer, William. *William Faulkner's First Book: "The
        Marble Faun," Fifty Years Later.* Memphis: The Pigeon
        Roost Press, 1974. Paper with wrapper. Catalogue of
        known copies with publishing history. Illustrations.

340   Daniel, Robert W. *A Catalogue of the Writings of Wil-
        liam Faulkner.* New Haven: Yale University Library,
        Summer 1942. "Published on the Occasion of an Exhi-
        bition in the Yale University Library." VC 2762. An-
        notated. Of significance are the annotations of *The
        Marble Faun, Sherwood Anderson & Other Famous
        Creoles,* and *A Green Bough.*

341   Massey, Linton R. *"Man Working," 1919-1962: Wil-
        liam Faulkner: A Catalogue of the William Faulkner
        Collections at the University of Virginia.* Introduction
        by John C. Wyllie. Charlottesville: The Bibliographical
        Society of the University of Virginia and the University
        Press of Virginia, [1968]. A guide to primary and sec-
        ondary sources. Four copies: one inscribed "For Mr.
        William B. Wisdom,/with much envy and admiration/
        for his skill and acuity as a/book collector/Linton Mas-
        sey/4 October 1968"; a second is annotated in the
        margins to indicate holdings of the Wisdom Collection.

342   Meriwether, James B. *The Literary Career of William
        Faulkner: A Bibliographical Study.* Princeton, New Jer-
        sey: Princeton University Library, 1961. VC 2766. One

of the two major catalogues of Faulkner's works. Three copies: one inscribed "This small contribution to/the best William Faulkner/collection in private hands/is inscribed for/William Bell Wisdom/with the warm regards of/the compiler:/James B. Meriwether/September 1961."

343   ———. "The Literary Career of William Faulkner: Catalogue of an Exhibition in the Princeton University Library." *The Princeton University Library Chronicle,* 21, No. 3 (Spring 1960), 111-164. VC 2768. Three copies: one inscribed "For William B. Wisdom/This very minor addition/To his very major Faulkner collection/with the warm regards/of the compiler/Jim Meriwether."

344   ———. *William Faulkner: A Check List.* Princeton, New Jersey: Princeton University Library, 1957. VC 2770. Signed on p. 2 by the compiler. Lists Faulkner's published writings. Reprint from *The Princeton University Library Chronicle,* 18, No. 3 (Spring 1957). See 345.

345   *The Princeton University Library Chronicle,* 18, No. 3 (Spring 1957). Special Faulkner issue, ed. James B. Meriwether. Signed exhibit program included. Signed by the editor and inscribed to William B. Wisdom. Two copies: the second unsigned. See 344.

346   Sleeth, Irene Lynn. *William Faulkner: A Bibliography of Criticism.* The Swallow Pamphlets Number 13. Denver, Colorado: Alan Swallow, [1962]. Authoritative through 1961 for American criticism. Includes selected foreign criticism. Three copies.

347   Texas, University of. *William Faulkner: An Exhibition of Manuscripts.* Austin: University of Texas, The Research Center, 1959. VC 2790. Two copies.

348   Virginia, University of. *Man Collecting: Manuscripts and Printed Works of William Faulkner in the University of Virginia Library.* Charlottesville: University of Virginia Library, [1975]. An exhibition honoring Linton Reynolds Massey.

348a ———. *William Faulkner: Man Working, 1919-1959.* Charlottesville: Alderman Library, 1959. VC 2791.

XIX. CORRESPONDENCE AND DOCUMENTS RELATING TO THE WILLIAM B. WISDOM COLLECTION OF WILLIAM FAULKNER

349   Brooks, Cleanth. Letter to William B. Wisdom. April 29, 1969. Refers to a printed lecture on Faulkner delivered in Helsinki and a completed chapter on Faulkner.

350   Cerf, Bennett. Letter to William B. Wisdom. April 25, 1951. Transmission accompanying copies of the Nobel Prize Address.

351   ———. Letter to William B. Wisdom. July 9, 1951. Comments on the demand for reprints of the Nobel Prize Address and indicates that there will be no more reprints made.

352   Cohn, Marguerite A. Letter to William B. Wisdom. July 26, 1951. Publishing information on *College Omnibus* and Nobel Prize Address pamphlets.

353   Collins, Carvel. Letter to William B. Wisdom. n.d. [c.November 1951]. On the special *Harvard Advocate* issue devoted to Faulkner.

354   ———. Letter to William B. Wisdom. June 21, 1953. Indicates making a "find" based on the text of *Mayday* in its relation to other books by Faulkner.

355   ———. Note to William B. Wisdom. February 25, 1954. Identifies the *Furioso* piece as Faulkner's "Afternoon of a Cow by Ernest V. Trueblood." See 102.

356   ———. Letter to William B. Wisdom. October 14, 1957. Refers vaguely to a copy of a letter by Faulkner.

357   ———. Note to William B. Wisdom. May 20, 1968. Acknowledges use of MSS. for the Random House revision of *New Orleans Sketches* and the attached copies of "The Lilacs" and "The Mirror of Chartres Street."

358   Friend, Julius W. Note. n.d. Indicates lines missing in MS. of "The Lilacs."

359   ———. Letter to William B. Wisdom. August 24, 1962. Letter of transmittal of MSS., "The Lilacs" and "The Mirror of Chartres St."

360   ———. Note on packing envelope. n.d. Refers to textual errors in "Frankie and Johnny." Other comments.

361   Massey, Linton. Letter to William B. Wisdom. October 28, 1968. Refers to gift of *Man Working* and copy of the Faulkner letter to Ben Wasson on *The Sound and the Fury.*

362   List of Faulkner publications. Typed. 2p.

363   List of typescripts in Wisdom Collection and related notes. 6p.

364   Price, Evelyn J. Letter to William B. Wisdom. May 20, 1970. Refers to Faulkner's Tallahatchie River Soil Conservation District Agreement. See 211.

365   Riever, J. W. Letter to William B. Wisdom. November 28, 1955. Regarding Faulkner's contribution to *Mis-*

sissippi Verse and mention of Faulkner in Oxford Chamber of Commerce publication. See 308.

366   Wiley, Bell I. Note to Connie Griffith. July 7, 1970. Eyewitness account of Faulkner's presentation on segregation before the Southern Historical Association in Memphis, Tennessee, November 10, 1955. See 167.

367   Wisdom, William B. Letter to Mrs. Evelyn J. Price. May 14, 1970. Requests copy of Faulkner's farm plan.

368   ———. Letter to Travis King. May 18, 1970. Inquiry about existence of a printed version of the farm plan.

369   ———. List of *Double Dealer* issues. Script. n.d. n.s. 2p. Issues with Faulkner indicated. Xerox copy with additional notes attached.

CHECKLIST OF OTHER FAULKNER MATERIALS IN THE TULANE UNIVERSITY LIBRARY

WORKS BY FAULKNER

I. NOVELS

Absalom, Absalom! New York: Modern Library, 1951. Introd. by Harvey Breit.

As I Lay Dying. New York: Jonathan Cape and Harrison Smith, 1930.

As I Lay Dying. New York: Random House, 1964.

A Fable. New York: Random House, 1954.

The Hamlet. New York: Random House, 1940. Title page illustrated in color.

The Hamlet. New York: Random House, 1956.

The Hamlet. New York: Random House, 1964. Third edition.

Intruder in the Dust. New York: Random House, 1948.

Intruder in the Dust. New York: Modern Library, 1948.

Light in August. New York: Smith and Haas, 1932.

Light in August. New York: Modern Library, 1950. Introd. by Richard H. Rovere.

Light in August. New York: Modern Library, 1959.

Light in August. New York: Vintage, 1972.

The Mansion. New York: Random House, 1959.

Mosquitoes. Garden City, New York: The Sun Dial Press, 1937.

Pylon. New York: Smith and Haas, 1935. "First printing, February, 1935."

The Reivers, A Reminiscence. New York: Random House, 1962.

Requiem for a Nun. New York: Random House, 1951.

Sanctuary. Collation of the original: 103 galley proofs. Unrevised of the first edition published by Smith in 1931. Film.

Sanctuary. New York: Modern Library, 1932. Introd. by William Faulkner.

Sanctuary. New York: Modern Library, 1958.

Sanctuary. New York: Random House, 1962.

Sartoris. New York: Random House, 1956.

Soldiers' Pay. New York: Boni and Liveright, 1926.

The Sound and the Fury. New York: Jonathan Cape and Harrison Smith, 1929.

The Sound and the Fury. New York: Modern Library, 1956.

The Sound and the Fury. New York: Random House, 1956. "Reproduced photographically from a copy of the first printing . . . 1929."

The Sound and the Fury. New York: Vintage, 1956. Appendix by Malcolm Cowley. "Reproduced photographically from a copy of the first printing . . . 1929."

The Town. New York: Random House, 1957.

The Unvanquished. New York: Random House, 1938. "First printing." Drawings by Edward Shenton.

The Unvanquished. New York: New American Library, 1959. Foreword by Carvel Collins.

The Wild Palms. New York: Random House, 1939. "First printing."

II.   SHORT STORIES: COLLECTIONS

Big Woods. New York: Random House, 1955.

Collected Stories. New York: Random House, 1950.

Doctor Martino and Other Stories. New York: Harrison Smith and Robert Haas, 1934.

William Faulkner: Early Prose and Poetry. Comp. and Introd. by Carvel Collins. London: Jonathan Cape, 1962.

William Faulkner: Early Prose and Poetry. Comp. and Introd. by Carvel Collins. Boston: Little, Brown, 1962. First edition.

The Faulkner Reader: Selections from the Works of William Faulkner. New York. Random House, 1954.

Go Down, Moses. New York: Modern Library, 1955.

Idyll in the Desert. Xerox copy. New York: Random House, 1941 edition. No. 387 of 400.

Jealousy and Episode: Two Stories. Minneapolis, Minnesota: Faulkner Studies, 1955. No. 240 of 500 copies. Both stories appeared originally in the *Times-Picayune* on March 1 and on August 16, 1925, respectively.

Knight's Gambit. New York: Random House, 1966.

Miss Zilphia Gant. Dallas: The Book Club of Texas, 1932. Xerox reproduction, 1961.

New Orleans Sketches. Edited and with notes by Ichiro Nishizaki. Tokyo: Hokuseido, 1953. Introd. and notes in Japanese and English.

New Orleans Sketches. Introd. by Carvel Collins. New Brunswick, New Jersey: Rutgers University Press, 1958.

New Orleans Sketches. Ed. Carvel Collins. New York: Random House, 1968.

Notes on a Horsethief. Greenville, Mississippi: Levee Press, 1950. Decorations by Elizabeth Calvert.

The Portable Faulkner. Ed. Malcolm Cowley. New York: Viking, 1946.

The Portable Faulkner. Ed. Malcolm Cowley. New York: Viking, 1967. Revised and expanded.

These 13. New York: Jonathan Cape and Harrison Smith, 1931.

These 13. London: Chatto & Windus, 1958. Volume Two of the series Collected Short Stories.

III. VERSE

A Green Bough. New York: Harrison Smith and Robert Haas, 1933.

The Marble Faun. Boston: The Four Seas Company, [1924]. Inscribed: "To Buddy/from Pappy./William Faulkner,/Oxford, Miss./4 Jul 1960." Signed on endpaper: "C.S. Franklin./1925."

Salmagundi. Milwaukee, Wisconsin: The Casanova Press, 1932. No. 6 of 525 copies.

This Earth: A Poem. New York: Equinox, 1932. Xerox reprint, 1961. Drawings by Albert Heckman.

IV. PLAYS

Ford, Ruth. *Requiem for a Nun, a Play from the Novel by William Faulkner.* New York: Random House, 1959.

V. ESSAYS AND ARTICLES

Essays, Speeches, and Public Letters. Ed. James B. Meriwether. New York: Random House, 1965.

Faulkner, William, Benjamin Mays, and Cecil Sims. *The Segregation Decisions: Papers Read at a Session of the Twenty-first Annual Meeting of the Southern Historical Association, Memphis, Tennessee, November 10, 1955.* Atlanta, Georgia: Southern Regional Council, 1956. Foreword by Bell I. Wiley.

Spratling, William P. and William Faulkner. *Sherwood Anderson & Other Famous Creoles: A Gallery of Contemporary New Orleans.* New Orleans: The Pelican Bookshop Press, 1926. Two copies: No. 57 of 250 copies; a second autographed but unnumbered.

————. *Sherwood Anderson & Other Famous Creoles: A Gallery of Contemporary New Orleans.* New Orleans: Pelican Bookshop Press, 1927. Second issue of 150 copies.

[74]

VI. INTERVIEWS

Faulkner at Nagano. Ed. Robert A. Jelliffe. Tokyo: Kenkyusha, 1956. First edition.

Faulkner at West Point. Eds. Joseph L. Fant, III, and Robert Ashley. New York: Random House, 1964.

Faulkner in the University: Class Conferences at the University of Virginia, 1957-1958. Eds. Frederick L. Gwynn and Joseph L. Blotner. Charlottesville: University of Virginia Press, 1959.

VII. LETTERS

Cowley, Malcolm. *The Faulkner-Cowley File: Letters and Memories, 1944-1962.* New York: Viking Press, 1966.

Faulkner, William. *Selected Letters of . . . .* Ed. Joseph Blotner. New York: Random House, 1977.

WORKS ABOUT FAULKNER

VIII. CRITICISM AND COMMENTARY

Adams, Richard P. *Faulkner: Myth and Motion.* Princeton, New Jersey: Princeton University Press, 1968.

Backman, Melvin. *Faulkner, the Major Years: A Critical Study.* Bloomington: Indiana University Press, 1966.

Barth, J. Robert, ed. *Religious Perspectives in Faulkner's Fiction: Yoknapatawpha and Beyond.* South Bend, Indiana: University of Notre Dame Press, 1972.

Bassett, John, ed. *William Faulkner: The Critical Heritage.* London and Boston: Routledge and K. Paul, 1975.

Beck, Warren. *Faulkner: Essays.* Madison: University of Wisconsin Press, 1976.

————. *Man in Motion: Faulkner's Trilogy.* Madison: University of Wisconsin Press, 1961.

Bedell, George C. *Kierkegaard and Faulkner: Modalities of Existence.* Baton Rouge: Louisiana State University Press, 1972.

Benedetti, Mario. *Marcel Proust y otros ensayos.* Montevideo: Numero, 1951. Part 3 on Faulkner.

Bleikasten, André and Roger Little, tr. *Faulkner's As I Lay Dying.* Bloomington: Indiana University Press, 1973. Revised and enlarged edition.

————. *The Most Splendid Failure: Faulkner's The Sound and the Fury.* Bloomington: Indiana University Press, 1976.

Bradford, M.E. "Faulkner and the Great White Father," *Louisiana Studies,* 3 (Winter 1964), 323-329. On the uses of Indians.

Brooks, Cleanth. *William Faulkner: The Yoknapatawpha Country.* New Haven: Yale University Press, 1964.

————. *William Faulkner: Toward Yoknapatawpha and Beyond.* New Haven: Yale University Press, 1978.

Broughton, Panthea Reid. *William Faulkner: The Abstract and the Actual.* Baton Rouge: Louisiana State University Press, 1974.

Brown, Calvin. *A Glossary of Faulkner's South.* New Haven: Yale University Press, 1976. Important for its glosses of the Southern vernacular.

Brylowski, Walter. *Faulkner's Olympian Laugh: Myth in the Novels*. Detroit, Michigan: Wayne State University Press, 1968.

Bungert, Hans. *William Faulkner und die humoristische Tradition des amerikanischen Südens*. Heidelberg: C. Winter, 1971. Summary in English.

Capps, Jack L. *As I Lay Dying: A Concordance to the Novel*. Introd. by Cleanth Brooks. West Point, New York: Faulkner Concordance Advisory Board and Ann Arbor Michigan: University Microfilms International, 1977.

Christadler, Martin. *Natur und Geschichte in Werk von William Faulkner*. Heidelberg: C. Winter, 1962.

Coindreau, Maurice. *The Time of William Faulkner: A French View of Modern American Fiction, Essays*. George M. Reeves, ed. and tr. Columbia: University of South Carolina Press, 1971. Forward by Michael Gresset.

Dabney, Lewis M. *The Indians of Yoknapatawpha: A Study in Literature and History*. Baton Rouge: Louisiana State University Press, 1974.

Dain, Martin J. *Faulkner's County: Yoknapatawpha*. New York: Random House, 1964.

Everett, Walter K. *Faulkner's Art and Characters*. Woodbury, N.Y.: Barron's Educational Series, 1969.

Fadiman, Regina K. *Faulkner's Intruder in the Dust: Novel into Film: The Screen Play by Ben Maddow as Adapted for Film by Clarence Brown*. Knoxville: University of Tennessee Press, 1978.

[77]

————. *Faulkner's Light in August: A Description and Interpretation of the Revisions.* Charlottesville: The Bibliographical Society of the University of Virginia and the University Press of Virginia, 1975.

Faulkner Studies, 1-3 (Spring 1952-Winter 1954). Published in Minneapolis, Minnesota. Superceded by *Critique: Studies in Modern Fiction.*

Faulkner: Three Studies. Special Issue of *The Emporia State Research Studies,* 11, No. 1 (September 1962). Essays by Robert L. Dorsch, Dorothy Greer, and Sherland N. Dirkson.

Ford, Margaret P. and Suzanne Kincaid. *Who's Who in Faulkner.* Baton Rouge: Louisiana State University Press, 1963.

Giannitrapani, Angela. *Wistaria: Studi Faulkneriani.* Napoli: Instituto Universitario Orientale, 1963.

Gold, Joseph. *William Faulkner: A Study in Humanism, from Metaphor to Discourse.* Norman: University of Oklahoma Press, 1966.

Goldman, Arnold, ed. *Twentieth Century Interpretations of Absalom, Absalom!: A Collection of Critical Essays.* Englewood Cliffs, N.J.: Prentice-Hall, 1971.

Guérard, Albert Joseph. *The Triumph of the Novel: Dickens, Dostoevsky, Faulkner.* New York: Oxford University Press, 1976.

Guetti, James L. *The Limits of Metaphor: A Study of Melville, Conrad, and Faulkner.* Ithaca, N.Y.: Cornell University Press, 1967. Treats *Absalom, Absalom!*

[78]

Harrington, Evans and Ann J. Abadie., eds. *The South and Faulkner's Yoknapatawpha: The Actual and the Apocryphal.* Jackson: University Press of Mississippi, 1977.

Hoffman, Frederick John. *William Faulkner.* TUSAS, 1. New York: Twayne, 1966. Second edition, revised.

Hoffman, Frederick John and Olga Vickery, eds. *William Faulkner: Two Decades of Criticism.* East Lansing: Michigan State College Press, 1951.

Hogan, Patrick G. "Faulkner's New Orleans Idiom: A Style in Embryo." *Louisiana Studies,* 5 (Fall 1966), 171-181. Re *New Orleans Sketches.*

Holman, Clarence Hugh. *Three Modes of Southern Fiction: Ellen Glasgow, William Faulkner, Thomas Wolfe.* Athens: University of Georgia Press, 1966.

Holmes, Edward M. *Faulkner's Twice Told Tales: His Re-use of His Material.* The Hague: Mouton, 1966.

Howe, Irving. *William Faulkner: A Critical Study.* New York: Vintage, 1952. Second edition, revised and expanded.

————. *William Faulkner: A Critical Study.* Chicago: University of Chicago Press, 1975. Third edition, revised and expanded.

Irwin, John T. *Doubling and Incest, Repetition and Revenge: A Speculative Reading of Faulkner.* Baltimore: Johns Hopkins University Press, 1975.

Jarrett-Kerr, Martin. *William Faulkner: A Critical Essay.* Grand Rapids, Michigan: Eerdman's, 1970.

Jehlen, Myra. *Class and Character in Faulkner's South.* New York: Columbia University Press, 1976.

Kerr, Elizabeth M. *Yoknapatawpha: Faulkner's "Little Postage Stamp of Native Soil."* New York: Fordham University Press, 1969.

Kinney, Arthur J. *Faulkner's Narrative Poetics . . . .* Amherst: University of Massachusetts Press, 1978.

Kirk, Robert W. *Faulkner's People: A Complete Guide and Index to Characters in the Fiction of William Faulkner.* Berkeley: University of California Press, 1963.

Langford, Gerald. *Faulkner's Revision of Absalom, Absalom! A Collation of the Manuscript and the Published Book.* Austin: University of Texas Press, 1971. Includes facsimiles of the texts.

————. *Faulkner's Revision of Sanctuary: A Collation of the Unrevised Galleys and the Published Book.* Austin: University of Texas Press, 1972.

Levins, Lynn G. *Faulkner's Heroic Design: The Yoknapatawpha Novels.* Athens: University of Georgia Press, 1976.

Longley, John L. *The Tragic Mask: A Study of Faulkner's Heroes.* Chapel Hill: University of North Carolina Press, 1963.

McHaney, Thomas L. *William Faulkner's The Wild Palms: A Study.* Jackson: University Press of Mississippi, 1975.

Malin, Irving. *William Faulkner: An Interpretation.* Stanford: Stanford University Press, 1957.

Meindl, Dieter. *Bewusstsein als Schicksal zu Struktur und Entwicklung von William Faulkners Generationenromanen.* Stuttgart: Metzler, 1974. Summary in English.

Michel, Laurence A. *The Thing Contained: Theory of the Tragic.* Bloomington: Indiana University Press, 1970.

Millgate, Michael. *The Achievement of William Faulkner.* London: Constable, 1966.

————. *The Achievement of William Faulkner.* Lincoln: University of Nebraska Press, 1978.

————. *William Faulkner.* New York: Grove Press, 1961.

————. *William Faulkner.* New York: Capricorn, 1971.

Miner, Ward L. *The World of William Faulkner.* New York: Pageant, 1959.

Minter, David L. ed. *Twentieth Century Interpretations of Light in August: A Collection of Critical Essays.* Englewood Cliffs, N.J.: Prentice-Hall, 1970.

O'Connor, William Van. *The Tangled Fire of William Faulkner.* Minneapolis: University of Minnesota Press, 1954.

————. *William Faulkner.* Minneapolis: University of Minnesota Press, 1959.

————. *William Faulkner.* Minneapolis: University of Minnesota Press, 1964. Revised edition.

Page, Sally R. *Faulkner's Women: Characterization and Meaning.* Deland, Fla.: Everett/Edwards, 1972.

Peavy, Charles D. *Go Slow Now: Faulkner and the Race Question*. Eugene: University of Oregon Press, 1971.

Pitavy, François and Gillian E. Cook, tr. *Faulkner's Light in August*. Bloomington: Indiana University Press, 1973. Revised and enlarged edition.

Reed, Joseph W. *Faulkner's Narrative*. New Haven: Yale University Press, 1973.

Richardson, Harold E. *William Faulkner: The Journey to Self-Discovery*. Columbia: University of Missouri Press, 1969.

Richardson, Kenneth E. *Force and Faith in the Novels of William Faulkner*. The Hague, Paris: Mouton, 1967.

Robb, Mary Cooper. *William Faulkner: An Estimate of His Contribution to the Modern American Novel*. Pittsburgh: University of Pittsburgh Press, 1957.

Runyan, Harry. *A Faulkner Glossary*. New York: Citadel Press, 1964.

Sachs, Viola. *Le Blanc et le noir chez Melville et Faulkner: ouvrage collectif*. Paris: Mouton, 1974.

Schoenberg, Estella. *Old Tales and Talking: Quentin Compson in William Faulkner's Absalom, Absalom! and Related Works*. Jackson: University Press of Mississippi, 1977.

Slatoff, Walter J. *Quest for Failure: A Study of William Faulkner*. Ithaca, N.Y.: Cornell University Press, 1960.

Smart, George K. *Religious Elements in Faulkner's Early Novels: A Selective Concordance*. Coral Gables, Fla.: University of Miami Press, 1965.

Swiggart, Peter. *The Art of Faulkner's Novels*. Austin: University of Texas Press, 1962.

Thompson, Lawrance Roger. *William Faulkner: An Introduction and Interpretation*. New York: Barnes and Noble, 1963.

Tuck, Dorothy. *Crowell's Handbook of Faulkner*. Advisory ed. Lewis Leary. New York: Crowell, 1964.

――――. *A Handbook of Faulkner*. London: Chatto and Windus, 1965.

Ulich, Michaela. *Perspektive und Erzahlstruktur in William Faulkners Romanen von The Sound and the Fury bis Intruder in the Dust*. Heidelberg: C. Winter, 1972.

Vickery, Olga W. *The Novels of William Faulkner: A Critical Interpretation*. Baton Rouge: Louisiana State University Press, 1964.

Volpe, Edmond L. *A Reader's Guide to William Faulkner*. New York: Farrar, Straus, 1964.

Waggoner, Hyatt H. *William Faulkner: From Jefferson to the World*. Lexington: University of Kentucky Press, 1966.

Wagner, Linda W. *Hemingway and Faulkner: Inventors/Masters*. Metuchen, N.J.: Scarecrow Press, 1975.

――――. *William Faulkner: Four Decades of Criticism*. East Lansing: Michigan State University Press, 1973.

Warren, Robert Penn, ed. *Faulkner: A Collection of Critical Essays*. Englewood Cliffs, N.J.: Prentice-Hall, 1966.

Watkins, Floyd C. *The Flesh and the Word: Eliot, Hemingway, Faulkner*. Nashville, Tenn.: Vanderbilt University Press, 1971.

―――. *William Faulkner: The Individual and the World* and Louise Cowan. *The Communal World of Southern Literature*. Lamar Memorial Lectures, 1960. n.p., 1960.

Watson, James Gray. *The Snopes Dilemma: Faulkner's Trilogy*. Coral Gables, Fla.: University of Miami Press, 1970.

Weber, Robert W. *Die Aussage der Form: zur Textur U. Struktur d. Bewusstseinsromans*. Heidelberg: C. Winter, 1969.

Weisgerber, Jean. *Faulkner and Dostoevsky: Influence and Confluence*. Tr. Dean McWilliams. Athens: Ohio University Press, 1974.

―――. *Faulkner et Dostoievski: confluences et influences*. Bruxelles: Presses Universitaires de Bruxelles; and Paris: Presses Universitaires de France, 1968.

William Faulkner Issue. *The Harvard Advocate*. Cambridge, Mass., 1951. Xerox reproduction of Vol. 135, No. 2.

Williams, David L. *Faulkner's Women: the Myth and the Muse*. McGill-Queen's University Press, 1977.

Wolfe, George H. *Faulkner: Fifty Years After The Marble Faun*. University: University of Alabama Press, 1976. Includes an essay by Richard P. Adams presented at a symposium at the University of Alabama in October of 1974.

Woodworth, Stanley D. *William Faulkner en France: panorama critique, 1931-1952.* Paris: Lettres Modernes, 1959.

Ziegler, Heide. *Existentielles Erleben und kurzes Erzählen: d. Komische, Tragische, Groteske u. Mythische in William Faulkner's Short Stories.* Stuttgart: Metzler, 1977.

IX. DISSERTATIONS AND THESES

Abelman, Franklin M. "Requiem for a Nun: An Experiment in Drama and Narration." Thesis (B.A.). 1964.

Castille, Philip. "Faulkner's Early Heroines." Diss. 1977.

DeCuir, Jene J. "The Poetry of *The Sound and the Fury.*" Thesis. 1968.

Firmin, Suzanne. "The Faulkners and the Southern Code of Honor." Thesis. 1961.

Florey, James B. "William Faulkner: Adumbration of Message with Mode of Voice." Thesis (B.A.). 1970.

Ford, Oliver J. "Elements of Marlowe's *Dr. Faustus* in Faulkner's *The Reivers.*" Thesis. 1967.

Gribbin, Daniel V. "The Influence of Henri Bergson on the Early Novels of William Faulkner." Thesis (B.A.). 1967.

Gurtman, Jane. "Una Comparación entre *El Luto humano,* por José Revueltas, y *As I Lay Dying,* por William Faulkner." Thesis (B.A.). 1974.

Herman, Myron S. " 'To Endure and Prevail': The Optimism of *The Sound and The Fury, Sanctuary, As I Lay Dying,* and *Light in August.*" Thesis. 1965.

[85]

Higgins, William R. "William Faulkner: Endurance and *Arete*." Thesis. 1959.

Howell, John M. "The Wasteland Tradition in the American Novel." Diss. 1963. Re *The Sound and the Fury*.

Julian, Jane Dickinson. "Faulkner's Man in Action: The Effective Word." Thesis. 1969.

Klosson, Kraig. "Patterns of Growth in *Light in August*." Thesis (B.A.). 1961.

Krefft, James H. "The Yoknapatawpha Indians: Fact and Fiction." Diss. 1976.

Lawson, Richard A. "Patterns of Initiation in William Faulkner's *Go Down, Moses*." Diss. 1966.

Logan, Elizabeth A. "A Study of Robert L. Flynn's *Journey to Jefferson:* An Adaptation of William Faulkner's *As I Lay Dying*." Thesis. 1967.

McClung, James W. "*As I Lay Dying* and *Light in August:* Counterpoint in Perspective and Counterpoint in Plot." Thesis. 1965.

McDowell, Richard. "Faulkner's Trilogy: A Reevaluation." Diss. 1977.

Madron, Beverly Brown. "The Relationship Between Poe's Tales of Ratiocination and Faulkner's *Knight's Gambit*." Thesis. 1970.

Millner, Gladys Welch. "Faulkner's Young Protagonists: The Innocent and the Damned." Diss. 1970.

―――. "The Sense of Guilt and Isolation in Faulkner and Warren." Thesis. 1965.

Pebworth, Ted L. "Emerson and Faulkner: Some Problems of the Romantic Artist in America." Thesis. 1958.

Rohrberger, Mary H. "William Faulkner's Fiction." Thesis. 1952. With genealogical tables.

Stewart, George G. "The Southern Yeomanry in the Faulknerian Myth." Thesis. 1960.

Wyde, Richard. "Mr. Compson's Influence on Quentin in *The Sound and the Fury.*" Thesis (B.A.). 1974.

Zeanah, Charles H. "Modernizing the Southern Myth: The Development of Gavin Stevens." Thesis (B.A.). 1973.

X. BIOGRAPHICAL, ANECDOTAL, AND TOPICAL MATERIAL

Blotner, Joseph L. *Faulkner: A Biography.* 2 vols. New York: Random House, 1974. First edition.

Cofield, Jack. *William Faulkner: the Cofield Collection.* Introd. by Carvel Collins. Oxford, Mississippi: Yoknapatawpha Press, 1978.

Falkner, Murry C. *The Falkners of Mississippi: A Memoir.* Baton Rouge: Louisiana State University Press, 1967.

Faulkner, John. *My Brother Bill: An Affectionate Reminiscence.* New York: Trident Press, 1963.

Louisiana Scrapbook. Vol. 53, 12-13. Clippings from *The Times-Picayune* re Faulkner in the French Quarter in the 1920's. Photographs.

Louisiana Scrapbook. Vol. 55, 2-3, 36-37. Clippings from *The Times-Picayune* re Faulkner, *Double Dealer,* and *New Orleans Sketches.* Illustrations.

Louisiana Scrapbook. Vol. 64, 28. Clipping from *The Times-Picayune* of July 7, 1962 in response to Faulkner's death the previous day. Includes photographs made in New Orleans in 1920's, 1939, and 1951.

Published photographs of William Faulkner: three clippings.

Scott Papers. Letter from Natalie Scott to Lyle Saxon, October 29, 1928. Re Faulkner in New Orleans.

Webb, James W. and A. Wigfall Green, eds. *William Faulkner of Oxford.* Baton Rouge: Louisiana State University Press, 1965.

Wilde, Meta Carpenter. *A Loving Gentleman: The Love Story of William Faulkner and Meta Carpenter.* New York: Simon and Schuster, 1976.

XI. BIBLIOGRAPHY AND CATALOGUES AND PROGRAMS OF EXHIBITIONS

Bassett, John. *William Faulkner: An Annotated Checklist of Criticism.* New York: D. Lewis, 1972. First edition.

Boozer, William. *William Faulkner's First Book: The Marble Faun, Fifty Years Later.* Memphis: Pigeon Roost Press, 1974.

Capps, Jack L., ed. *The William Faulkner Collection at West Point and the Faulkner Concordances.* With an Introd. West Point, New York: United States Military Academy, 1974. Occasional Papers United States Military Academy Library, No. 2. Number 343 of a limited edition of 650 copies.

McHaney, Thomas L. *William Faulkner: A Reference Guide*. Boston: G. K. Hall, 1976.

Massey, Linton R. *"Man Working," 1919-1962: William Faulkner: A Catalogue of the William Faulkner Collections at the University of Virginia*. Charlottesville: The Bibliographical Society of the University of Virginia and the University Press of Virginia, 1968. Introduction by John C. Wyllie.

Meriwether, James B. *The Literary Career of William Faulkner: A Bibliographical Study*. Princeton: Princeton University Library, 1961.

Petersen, Carl. *Each in Its Ordered Place: A Faulkner Collector's Notebook*. Ann Arbor: Ardis, 1975.

Sleeth, Irene L. *William Faulkner: A Bibliography of Criticism*. Denver: Swallow, 1962. Xerox copy.

Texas, University of. *William Faulkner: An Exhibition of Manuscripts*. Austin: University of Texas, Humanities Research Center, 1959.

Virginia, University of. *Man Collecting: Manuscripts and Printed Works of William Faulkner in the University of Virginia Library*. Charlottesville: University of Virginia Library, [1975].

XII. WORKS BY FAULKNER'S FAMILY NOT OTHERWISE CITED

Falkner, William C. *The White Rose of Memphis: A Novel*. New York: Caley Taylor, 1953. Introduction by Robert Cantwell.

Faulkner, John. *Ain't Gonna Rain No More*. Greenwich, Conn.: Fawcett, 1959. Autographed.

————. *Cabin Road*. New York: Fawcett, 1951. Autographed.

————. *Cabin Road*. Baton Rouge: Louisiana State University Press, 1969. Introduction by Redding S. Sugg, Jr.

————. *Chooky*. New York: Norton, 1950. First edition. Illustrated by Rafaello Busoni. Autographed.

————. *Men Working*. New York: Harcourt, Brace and Company, 1941. First edition.